Instructor's Manual to accompany Hyde:
UNDERSTANDING ■
HUMAN SEXUALITY

ELIZABETH ALLGEIER
Department of Psychology
State University of New York
at Fredonia

JANET SHIBLEY HYDE
Department of Psychology
Bowling Green State University

McGraw-Hill Book·Company
New York St. Louis San Francisco Auckland Bogotá Düsseldorf
Johannesburg London Madrid Mexico Montreal New Delhi Panama
Paris São Paulo Singapore Sydney Tokyo Toronto

TABLE OF CONTENTS

PREFACE

Much of the material contained in this manual (aside from the standard evaluation materials found in all IMs) is designed to help the teacher who is just beginning to teach the topic. Therefore, we want to suggest ways in which we have used this material, and we want to make a few comments on our experiences with teaching human sexuality.

ORGANIZATION OF THE MANUAL

The first 23 chapters of this manual correspond with the chapters in Hyde's text <u>Understanding Human Sexuality</u>, and each contains six sections.

The first section, <u>Learning Objectives</u>, is contained on a single page so that it may be xeroxed and distributed to students as an aid for exam preparation. Names of those researchers who are important in the area (and whose names may appear in the exam questions) are included. Students who can meet these objectives should do very well on the exams.

<u>Chapter at a Glance</u> has been written for the instructor. Although it is assumed that you will read the text, this section should be helpful to those of you who want to expand upon, but not duplicate, material presented in the text. The underlined portions correspond to headings and sub-headings in the text.

The <u>Glossary</u> is a listing of terms which may be problematic for students in the chapter and you may want to call their attention to the Glossary at the back of Hyde's text.

The section on <u>Audio-Visual Aids</u> contains brief descriptions of movies and tapes that are relevant to topics covered in the chapter. Film lengths and prices are included, however the addresses of the film distributors are listed at the end of the manual in Chapter 25. There is some additional information on several sexuality packages contained in that chapter.

<u>Demonstrations or Group Discussion</u> contains suggestions for class sessions. Since some of these take a little time to arrange (for instance, scheduling speakers or duplicating Values Clarification materials), you may want to consult this section well before your scheduled time for covering a given chapter.

The final section, <u>Evaluation Materials</u>, contains three or four main kinds of test items. The essay or research items may either be used on exams or may be used for the generation of a list of topics for student literature reviews or research topics. For many of these, students are asked to demonstrate their awareness of factual material from the text and then to give their opinions regarding some of the value-laden issues in the field. Page numbers are included where the relevant factual material may be found. The remaining items consist of multiple choice, and true/false items and, for some chapters, fill-in-the-blank or matching items. Again, page numbers indicating the source of the answer in the text have been provided.

We recommend that these be included on tests so that you may suggest that students look up the answer in the text <u>before</u> coming to argue with you about the test. In writing these items, we tried to avoid any "trick" questions and a number of them have been tested in our classes. Some items are very difficult ("picky") and for others, the answers are self-evident (included mainly to reinforce important points brought out in the text). Most, though, have been designed to be answered readily by conscientious students who take notes as they read.

Chapter 24 consists of a large number of test items which may be used for a comprehensive final. A <u>Learning Objectives</u> section has been provided for the final to help students prepare for it, and although it reflects the kind and level of information required to perform well on the final, you may want to modify it to reflect the level of information retention you feel is appropriate.

DISCIPLINARY FOCUS AND ASSIGNMENT OF READINGS

Human Sexuality is an unusual topic as it remains an interdisciplinary field to which psychologists, sociologists, biologists, educators, home economists, counselors, physicians, human developmentalists, and numerous others contribute information. Similarly, the course may be taught from a variety of disciplinary perspectives. Those of you in particular academic areas may wish to emphasize some sections of the text while deleting other areas in favor of providing more in-depth treatment of your discipline via assigned readings. For that reason, we have identified three groups of disciplines as a method of suggesting chapters which could be replaced with assigned readings.

Specifically, instructors in the areas of <u>Biology, Health,</u> and <u>Physical Education</u> might prefer to delete Chapters 16, 17, 20 and 21 (Rape; Love; Ethics, Religion, and Sexuality; and Sex and the Law). In their place, the instructor might assign the 16 articles from the Sexual Biology and Health section of <u>Readings in Human Sexuality</u> 78/79 (Guilford, Connecticut: Dushkin, 1978), as well as some of the other articles in the book.

<u>Psychologists</u> might prefer to delete Chapters 3, 19, 20 and 21 (Sex Hormones and Sexual Differentiation; Sexual Diseases; Ethics, Religion, and Sexuality; and Sex and the Law) in favor of many of the reports of social-psychological research in Byrne & Byrne's <u>Exploring Human Sexuality</u> (New York: Harper & Row, 1977).

Those teaching in departments of <u>Sociology, Home Economics, Human Development,</u> and <u>Religion,</u> might prefer to replace Chapters 2, 3 and 7 (Sexual Anatomy; Sex Hormones and Sexual Differentiation; and The Physiology of Sexual Response) with many of the articles from Gordon & Johnson's <u>Readings in Human Sexuality: Contemporary Perspectives</u> (New York: Harper & Row, 1976).

Finally, for those of you who haven't taught this course before, this is a delightful topic which presents the instructor with some unique opportunities (and some equally unique problems) for teaching. To begin with, not only is the subject matter intrinsically interesting to students, but the results of surveys that we've conducted indicate that it tends to attract students who already know more about the topic than do students of the same age enrolled in classes taught at the same level. The willingness of students to generate and to participate in discussion may provide you with an unusual problem: how to _end_ discussion at those times when you feel particularly committed to delivering a given body of material within the hour. Unannounced quizzes are unnecessary--in fact, the tendency of students to read ahead and ask questions in class may be an embarrassment to the unprepared teacher. In addition, the subject provides an excellent vehicle for getting across some of the nuts and bolts involved in the scientific method.

Your biggest difficulty will probably involve helping students to differentiate between value judgments and factual information. Some of the discussion questions are designed to help you accomplish that task.

We have one last bit of advice. If you are able to arrange your teaching schedule so that you end your day with human sexuality, any slight depression you may feel as an aftermath of earlier classes of passive, unprepared students will be eliminated by the energy and enthusiasm of your students in human sexuality. We hope that you enjoy teaching this course as much as we do. If you have any suggestions for improving this manual or questions about particular parts of it, please let us know.

E.R.A.
J.S.H.

CHAPTER 1: SEXUALITY IN PERSPECTIVE

I. LEARNING OBJECTIVES

Study of this chapter should enable the student to:

1. Specify some of the problems involved in distinguishing between the terms "sex" and "gender."

2. Compare and contrast different theoretical approaches to explaining sexuality.

3. Understand the Freudian concepts of id, ego, and superego in terms of how each influences sexual behavior.

4. Describe the erogenous zones involved in each of the stages of psychosexual development.

5. Compare the Oedipus and Electra complexes and the relationships between them and the Freudian notions of castration anxiety and penis envy.

6. Describe the differences between Freud and feminists in their explanations of female sexual expression.

7. Characterize the position taken by learning theorists regarding the development of sexual and gender role behavior.

8. Compare norms about sexual expression among the peoples of Inis Beag and Mangaia.

9. Contrast sexual attitudes and behavior in contemporary America with those in other cultures.

10. Indicate the extent to which other cultures share our standards regarding what is attractive.

11. Compare the sexual behavior considered appropriate for each gender in this culture versus other cultures.

12. Specify the ways in which our race and social class may be related to our sexual attitudes and behaviors.

13. Indicate how humans are similar to and different from other species in their sexual behavior.

14. Describe some of the ways in which sex is used for nonsexual purposes.

15. Describe the contributions of Freud, Ellis, Hirschfeld, Krafft-Ebing, Kinsey, Ford & Beach, and Masters & Johnson to our understanding of human sexuality.

1

II. CHAPTER AT A GLANCE

<u>Introduction</u> (p. 2)

<u>Sex and Gender</u> (pp. 2-3): Distinguishes between the two terms: "sex" refers to sexual anatomy and sexual behavior; "gender" refers to the state of being male or female. Notes that this is a book about sex, not gender. Covers Kinsey's definition of sex and provides the definition to be used in the text: "Behavior that produces arousal and increases the chance of orgasm."

<u>Understanding Sexuality</u> (pp. 3-5)
    <u>Religion</u>: Briefly describes viewpoints held by early Greeks, 15th century Christians, and Muslims. (More detailed discussion is in Ch. 20.)
    <u>Science</u>: Covers early contributions of biologists and physicians and the more recent work of Kinsey, Masters & Johnson, and several anthropologists.

<u>Theoretical Perspectives</u> (pp. 5-13)
    <u>Psychoanalytic Theory</u>: Defines libido, thanatos, and sublimation.
        <u>Id, ego, and superego</u>: Defines these, plus the pleasure and reality principles, and idealism. Describes the interactions.
        <u>Erogenous zones</u>: Defined.
        <u>Stages of psychosexual development</u>: Reviews the Freudian stages and discusses the Oedipus and Electra complexes, castration anxiety, and penis envy.
        <u>Freud on women</u>: Covers Freudian notions of female sexuality as masochistic; his vaginal/clitoral orgasm distinction, and notes feminist objections to these ideas.
        <u>Evaluation of psychoanalytic theory</u>
    <u>Sexuality as Motivation</u>: Defines need, motive, and drive, and distinguishes between the drives of sex and hunger.
    <u>Learning Theory</u>
        <u>Operant conditioning</u>: Definition of major concepts.
        <u>Behavior modification</u>: Describes the use of this approach and discusses aversion therapy.
        <u>Social learning</u>: Applied to learning of gender identification and imitation.
    <u>Humanistic Psychology</u>: Discusses Maslow's self-actualization and the human potential movement including encounter groups.
    <u>Transactional Analysis</u>: Reviews Berne's notions.
    <u>Sociological Theory</u>: Defines norms, institutions, socialization, and roles.

<u>Cross-Cultural Perspectives</u> (pp. 13-22): Brief review of Ford & Beach's (1951) study, notes that all societies regulate sexuality.
    <u>Generalizations</u>
    <u>Sexual Techniques</u>: Covers cross-cultural evidence on kissing, grooming, oral sex, pain infliction, and coital frequency.

Masturbation: Describes attitudes and behavior regarding male
   and female self-stimulation.
Homosexuality: Gives brief review and notes Ford & Beach's three
   generalizations.
Standards of Attractiveness: Notes the great variations, cross-
   culturally.
Gender Roles: Describes anthropological work.
Social Class and Ethnic Group Variations in the United States.
   Social class and sex: Reviews Kinsey's findings and Rain-
      water's work on sexuality in the lower class.
   Black sexuality: Compares black and white sexual attitudes
      and behavior.
The Significance of the Cross-Cultural Studies: Suggests that
   they demonstrate the enormous variation in sexual behavior
   and the importance of culture and learning in shaping our
   sexual behavior.

Cross-Species Perspectives (pp. 22-27)
   Masturbation: Describes primate, deer, and porcupine practices.
   Mouth-Genital Stimulation
   Homosexual Behavior: Notes that the behavior occurs in many
      other species.
   Human Uniqueness: Notes the trend from hormonal to nervous
      system (learning) control of sexual behavior as we move from
      lower to higher species. Applies this to female sexuality
      across species.
   The Nonsexual Uses of Sexual Behavior: Describes such uses as
      dominance, signaling the end of hostilities, economic and
      power gain. Reviews Cohen & Friedman's notions regarding
      adolescent uses of sex for peer approval, expression of
      hostility, rebellion, and escape.

Summary (pp. 27-28)

Suggestions for Further Reading (p. 28)

Focus:

   Sexuality in Two Societies: Inis Beag and Mangaia (pp. 16-17)

III. GLOSSARY

   Electra complex. In Freudian theory, the little girl's sexual
      desires for her father; the female analog of the Oedipus
      complex.

   libido. The sex drive.

   Oedipus complex. In Freudian theory, the sexual attraction of a
      little boy to his mother.

IV. AUDIO-VISUAL AIDS

Movies:

A quickie. Multi Media, #395, 1 min., 45 sec., B & W, 1970,
$35/$10. A "speeded up" version of a sexual encounter.
Very amusing, and helps to ease any initial nervousness
students may have with the course. Music only.

Mammalian Sexual Behavior. Kinsey Institute at Indiana University, B & W, silent, available for the cost of copying (about
$45 per reel), 2 reels. Shows the sexual behavior of many
mammalian species. Reel 2 is especially interesting, including an impressive view of elephants copulating, cats with the
after reaction of the female, and all-too-human chimpanzees.

Rich & Judy. Multi Media, #410, 12 min., color, 1971, $200/$35.
Portrayal of married couple enjoying oral sex and intercourse
by a swimming pool. Music only.

Tapes:

Harold T. Christensen-Cultures and sexual intimacy. Norton,
#350134, 25 min., $13.75. Premarital sexual behavior in 3
cultural groups.

Cultural Influences. Norton, #340082, 60 min., $13.75. Indi-
viduals from different countries discuss various cultural
attitudes toward virginity, premarital sex, homosexuality,
illegitimacy, the double standard, etc. Shows that all societies have used sex to serve a multitude of purposes and all
societies regulate the expression of sexuality.

Sexual Purposes and Patterns. #340015, 60 min., $13.75. Dis-
cusses purposes of sex including pleasure, tension release,
reproduction, reinforcement of identity, communication,
companionship, love, etc.

V. DEMONSTRATIONS OR GROUP DISCUSSION

A. Goals for the course: Ask students to write (anonymously)
their academic and nonacademic goals for the course plus any questions they hope to have answered during the semester. These questions may be used throughout the semester when covering relevant
topics. You may want to describe your own goals for the course as
well as note the objectives described in the preface of Understanding Human Sexuality.

B. Pretests of Sexual Attitudes, Behavior and Information: It
is often helpful to the instructor to know something about the
attitudes and experience of students in the course, as well as the

level of information they have coming into the course. The Attitudes and Behavior Questionnaire was written by the second author and has been used in her courses. The Sexual Knowledge Survey was written by A. R. Allgeier and is reproduced here with his permission. Both measures are shown on the following pages and may simply be xeroxed for students by the instructor.

SEXUAL ATTITUDES AND BEHAVIOR

Instructions: For all items, mark your answer in the blank at the left.

___Marital status: A. single   B. married   C. divorced, separated or widowed

___Age (in years)

___Class: A. Freshman   B. Sophomore   C. Junior   D. Senior

      E. Other

PART I. ATTITUDES

Instructions: Place the letter representing one of these 5 responses to indicate how you feel about the following kinds of sexual behavior.
- a. strongly approve
- b. approve somewhat
- c. neutral
- d. disapprove somewhat
- e. strongly disapprove

___1. Premarital sex when the couple are engaged.

___2. Premarital sex when the couple are in love.

___3. Premarital sex when the couple are only casually acquainted.

___4. Masturbation.

___5. Homosexuality.

___6. Extramarital sex (a married person having sex with someone other than their spouse).

___7. Mouth-genital sex (or oral-genital sex--cunnilingus or fellatio).

___8. Abortion: a. approve under certain circumstances such as rape or incest or when the woman's health is endangered; b. approve of abortion on demand (whenever a woman requests it); c. disapprove of abortion under any circumstances.

5

PART II. BEHAVIOR

___1. Have you ever engaged in premarital sexual intercourse?
a. yes; b. no.

___2. With how many partners have you had premarital sexual inter-
course? a. 0; b. 1; c. 2; d. 3-5; e. 6-10; f. 11-100;
g. 100 or more.

___3. At what age did you begin masturbating? a. under 10;
b. 10-12; c. 13-15; d. 16-18; e. 19 or over; f. have never
masturbated.

___4. Currently, about how many times per month do you masturbate?
a. once per month or less; b. 2-4 times per month; c. 5-10
times per month; d. more than 10 times per month.

___5. Have you experienced or engaged in fellatio? a. yes; b. no.

___6. Have you experienced or engaged in cunnilingus? a. yes;
b. no.

___7. Have you ever engaged in anal intercourse? a. yes; b. no.

___8. Have you ever had a sexual experience to orgasm with someone
of your own gender? a. yes; b. no.

___9. The last time you engaged in sexual intercourse, what form
of contraception was used? a. birth control pills; b. IUD;
c. diaphragm; d. condom (rubber); e. foam or jelly;
f. rhythm; g. nothing or don't know.

___10. How many times have you become pregnant or impregnated some-
one? a. never; b. once; c. twice; d. three or more times.

___11. How was the pregnancy resolved? a. abortion; b. the baby was
born and kept; c. the baby was born and adopted; d. not
applicable.

SEXUAL KNOWLEDGE SURVEY

This is a test of the accuracy of your knowledge about human sexual
behavior. Each of the following statements can be answered true or
false. Please answer all questions.

___1. A female can become pregnant during sexual intercourse with-
out the male having an orgasm.

___2. The balance of sexual hormones is the most frequent cause of
homosexuality.

____3. Women can become sexually aroused when breast-feeding an infant.

____4. A woman's chances of becoming pregnant are much greater if she experiences orgasm during sexual intercourse.

____5. Direct contact between the penis and the clitoris is necessary to produce female orgasm during sexual intercourse.

____6. There are no physiological differences in orgasms attained through sexual intercourse, masturbation, or any other technique.

____7. Males do not develop the capacity to attain an erection until they reach puberty (adolescence).

____8. The incest taboo is a result of social learning.

____9. Women are biologically more capable of multiple orgasms than are men.

____10. A hysterectomy (removal of the uterus) reduces a woman's sexual drive.

____11. There are two different types of physiological orgasms in women: clitoral and vaginal.

____12. The most sensitive area to sexual stimulation in most women is the clitoris.

____13. Erection of the nipples is often a sign of sexual arousal in the male.

____14. Homosexual behavior, masturbation, and fetishism occur among other species of animals besides humans.

____15. Different positions in sexual intercourse are practiced most often by persons in lower socioeconomic classes.

____16. In this culture, some homosexual behavior is often a normal part of growing up.

____17. A male is incapable of orgasm until he reaches puberty (adolescence).

____18. Sexual intercourse after the first six months of pregnancy may generally be practiced without endangering the health of the mother or the fetus.

____19. Sex criminals use pornographic material more often in their youth than the average person in their culture.

___20. Most prostitutes are nymphomaniacs.

___21. A majority of the sexual crimes committed against children are by adults who are friends or relatives of the victim.

___22. Almost all cases of impotency are of a psychological origin.

___23. The rhythm method is just as effective as the birth control pill in preventing conception.

___24. Social rather than biological factors determine the manner in which an individual's sexuality is expressed.

___25. Relatively few cases of "frigidity" are of a biological origin.

___26. Masturbation by a married person is usually related to marital problems.

___27. For a short period of time following orgasm, men are usually not able to respond to further sexual stimulation.

___28. Frequent masturbation is one of the most common causes of premature ejaculation in the male.

___29. During lovemaking it usually takes the female less time to become sexually aroused and reach climax than it does the male.

___30. An intact hymen (maidenhead, "cherry") is a reliable indicator of virginity.

___31. Sexual stimulation often causes erection of the nipple of the female breasts.

___32. Sexual gratification associated with the infliction of pain is called sadism.

___33. Circumcision makes it more difficult for a male to control ejaculation.

___34. Nocturnal emissions or "wet dreams" are indicative of sexual problems.

___35. Central nervous system damage can be one of the results of untreated, advanced syphilis.

___36. Transvestites are individuals who derive sexual excitement from dressing in the clothes of the opposite sex.

_____37. The castration of an adult results in a loss of his sex drive.

_____38. Almost all homosexuals can be identified by their physical characteristics.

_____39. Certain foods have been shown to be aphrodisiacs (sexual stimulants).

_____40. The most important factor in being able to maintain sexual activity during old age is a history of regular sexual activity.

<u>Answer key:</u> The following items are true: 1, 3, 6, 8, 9, 12, 13, 14, 16, 18, 21, 22, 24, 25, 27, 31, 32, 35, 36, 40.

C. Introductory Values Clarification Exercise: This exercise gets students thinking and talking about their own values about various sexual lifestyles and is a good way to open the course, particularly because the exercise is not very threatening. After passing out the descriptions of the nine characters (the descriptions are presented on the next page, and may be xeroxed by the instructor), ask the students to follow the directions on the top of the exercise. While the students are reading the exercise and ranking the characters, the instructor may post signs around the room, with each sign bearing the name of a different character. After the students have done their ranking, tell them to go and stand next to the sign of the person they liked or admired most. Have the cluster of people by each sign specify to the class why they chose that person. Then have the groups argue back and forth about the relative merits of their choices. After this, repeat for the person they liked or admired least. Finally, have all students return to their seats and reflect on what they learned from the exercise. They will probably note things such as there being a wider variety of opinions in the class than they would have thought, and that they heard some arguments for various positions that they had not heard before.

VALUES CLARIFICATION

Rank order the following people from 1 through 9 indicating a 1 for the person you most like or admire and a 9 for the person you least like or admire.

___VIRGINIA is a junior in college. She has decided to remain a virgin until she gets married. She is bright, attractive, dates frequently, is very affectionate, enjoys necking and petting, but always makes it very clear to all her dates that she won't have intercourse with them.

___IAN is a college senior. He is not a good looking person, nor does he have a sparkling personality, but he is a very nice, very considerate person. By the standards expected of males, he is relatively inexperienced. He has had intercourse with three women. They were all more experienced than he and made him feel somewhat inadequate. Right now, he feels very ambivalent about sex--he sees that there are a lot of rewards for it, gaining status, pleasure, etc., but he fears rejection and is afraid that he is inadequate.

___ANN is a college senior. She likes sex a lot. She has been sleeping with men since she was a senior in high school. She is not sure when or if she wants to get married, and prefers variety in her relationships, not getting tied down. She generally does not date any one man more than a month. She finds these brief relationships very enjoyable and has no ambivalence about her chosen life-style.

___AMY is a college senior. She has been sleeping with men since she was a senior in high school. She tries to get as much variety as possible, never dating any one man for more than a month. Every time she goes to bed with a man, it means to her that she is an attractive, desirable, adequate woman. But she soon tires of the relationship and feels a need to have her attractiveness reaffirmed by having sex with a new man. She feels somewhat unhappy in her lifestyle, but can't seem to find any satisfaction in long-term relationships.

___RICK is a college senior. He is very attractive, has a good personality, and is a B student. Women find him very attractive. He shows his dates a good time, taking them to dinner at a nice place. He enjoys sex and expects that his dates will go to bed with him, which they almost invariably do. He prefers to date a woman no more than 3 or 4 times, and then moves on to another. His status on campus is high because of his obvious success with women, and he enjoys this status and is very self-confident as a result.

___KAY is 40 and is in sales with a cosmetics manufacturer. She loves her husband and they have a good marriage. But when she is on business trips or at conventions, she often has a drink or two and goes to bed with one of the men there. She enjoys men and sex. She feels somewhat guilty about these flings, but not enough to stop. Her husband doesn't know about them, and her chief fear is that he will find out.

____JIM is 35 and a lawyer. He is a homosexual. He has been living with John for 8 years. They have a monogamous relationship and are quite happy and satisfied with each other. When Jim was in college, he had several affairs with women, but he found them unsatisfying. Later, he experimented with homosexuality. He met John, they fell in love, and have been happily "married" ever since. Jim's law practice is thriving, so that he is able to donate 2 evenings a week to giving legal assistance to welfare people. Jim is very happy with his sexual lifestyle and with his life generally.

____VIRGIL is a junior in college. He is 5'7" tall and average look-ing. He has dates 2 or 3 times a month, but has never asked a fe-male to go to bed with him, and he finds the aggressive way males treat females to be objectionable. As a result, he is a 21-year-old virgin and is becoming concerned about his total lack of sexual experience.

____JOYCE is a junior in college. She has been going with John for about a year and they have discussed the possibility of marriage sometime in the future, but probably not until he has completed medical school and she has gotten her Masters degree in social work. A month ago, Joyce discovered that she was pregnant. She and John discussed the matter and decided that she should have an abortion because their relationship was not yet stable enough to get married and a baby would ruin their chances for further education and good careers. Last week she had the abortion.

    D. Chanting Sexual Words: The following exercise may be used to do some desensitization work with students at the beginning of the sex course so that they will feel more free in talking about sex and will be more apt to use direct, precise terminology.
    Have the class, in unison, say a sexual word 5 or 10 times. Among the words you may want to use are penis, clitoris (good oppor-tunity for teaching the correct pronunciation of this one), inter-course, and masturbation.

    E. Further exercises: If you want more discussion section exer-cises, Values in Sexuality by E. S. Morrison and M. U. Price (New York: Hart, 1974) and Group Strategies in Understanding Human Sexuality: Getting in Touch by R. Kaplan, L. B. Meeks, & J. Segal (Dubuque, Iowa: Wm. C. Brown, 1978) are rich sources of ideas for exercises throughout the course.

VI. EVALUATION MATERIALS

Essay or research questions

1. Why did Freud believe that women were somewhat morally immature compared with men, and on what grounds do feminists object to his

position? (Pp. 7-8 for Freud's explanation; p. 8 for feminist objections.) What is your opinion, and why?

2. Compare the cultures of Inis Beag, Mangaia, and contemporary middle class America regarding the expression of adult sexuality. Which of the theoretical approaches do you think best accounts for the differences between the three cultures, and why? (Pp. 5-13 for theoretical positions; pp. 20-21 for middle class America; pp. 16-17 for focus on the other two cultures.)

3. Think about someone you've known who holds very strong attitudes (either "liberal" or "conservative") about premarital sexual intercourse. How would you explain his or her position via one of the theoretical perspectives? Do you find any of the research regarding the relationship between social class, racial or ethnic group membership and sexual behavior useful in understanding his or her behavior? Why or why not? (See pp. 5-13 for theoretical perspectives, pp. 20-22 for review of research on social class membership and race on sexual behavior; students may also look up "sexual attitudes" in Psychological Abstracts to find references to articles reporting current research on these variables.)

Multiple choice

1. The scientific study of sex began in the ___ century. a. mid 17th; b. late 18th; *c. late 19th; d. mid 20th. (p. 4)

2. The first sex research institute was founded by: a. Freud; b. Kinsey; c. Krafft-Ebing; *d. Hirschfeld; e. Ellis. (p. 5)

3. This early sex researcher was particularly interested in pathological sexual behavior. a. Hirschfeld; b. Kinsey; c. Ellis; d. Leeuwenhoek; *e. Krafft-Ebing. (p. 5)

4. The scientific study of sex (sexology) emerged as a separate, unified academic discipline (like psychology or sociology) in the ___ century. a. mid 19th; b. early 20th; c. mid 20th; *d. none of the above; it remains an interdisciplinary field of study. (p. 5)

5. In Freud's view of the personality, the ___ operates on the reality principle. a. id; *b. ego; c. superego; d. subego. (p. 6)

6. Last night, you really felt tempted to join ___ (imagine name of the object of your sexual desire) at a party. But you also wanted to get an A on this test. After thinking about the dilemma, you invited him/her to study with you last night and to go out to dinner with you tonight. According to Freud, you were first influenced by your ___, then by your___, and finally by

your ___. *a. id, superego, ego; b. id, ego, superego; c. ego, id, superego; d. superego, ego, id; e. superego, id, ego. (p. 6)

7. The ___ contains a set of instincts present at birth. *a. id; b. ego; c. superego; d. subego. (p. 6)

8. Freud would say that blushing at the sound of a 4-letter word is the result of the influence of the: a. id; b. ego; c. subego; *d. superego. (p. 6)

9. According to Freud, the Oedipus complex develops during the ___ stage: a. oral; b. anal; *c. phallic; d. latency; e. genital. (p. 7)

10. Freud suggested that, compared with males, females: a. have an easier time passing through the phallic stage; *b. are less morally mature; c. have more castration anxiety; d. have a stronger motive for resolving the Oedipus/Electra complex. (p. 7)

11. During latency, according to Freud, a child: a. desires his/her parent; *b. represses sexual impulses; c. is subconsciously motivated to be late all the time; d. desires people of the same gender; e. hates the parent of the same gender. (p. 7)

12. In ___ theory, females are inherently passive and males are inherently active, sexually. *a. psychoanalytic; b. social learning; c. sociological; d. humanistic; e. motivationist. (p. 8)

13. Most of the predictions arising from psychoanalytic theory: a. have been verified experimentally; b. give too little emphasis to the biological determinants of behavior; *c. cannot be tested via the usual scientific methods; d. ignore the role of subconscious determinants; e. both b & d. (p. 8)

14. The classic experiment in which male rats, deprived of sex, crossed an electrified grid to reach a female rat demonstrated: *a. the existence of a sex drive; b. that rats feel no pain from electric shock; c. that frequency of crossing was unrelated to length of deprivation; d. that scientists are voyeurs. (p. 9)

15. For a learning theorist, sexual activity is: a. a reinforcer; b. a reward; c. a behavior that is rewarded or punished; *d. all of the above. (p. 10)

16. The sex drive differs from the drive for hunger in that: a. in the absence of sex, there is no known way in which the body is depleted; b. sex is not necessary for individual survival; c. hunger needn't be controlled, whereas sex needs to be; *d. both a & b. (p. 9)

13

17. Hepzebah and Zeke are engaged in heavy petting in the living room when Hepzi's parents walk in. They ground her for a couple of weeks. According to learning theory, this is likely to: a. stop her from petting; b. have absolutely no effect on her petting behavior; *c. ensure that she'll avoid heavy petting in places where her parents will catch her; d. make Zeke impotent in the future. (pp. 10-11)

18. Hepzi's behavior (above question) when she's no longer grounded is due to the principle: a. that punishment eliminates behavior; b. of delay of reinforcement; *c. that punishment is not very effective in eliminating behavior--it is more likely to teach sneakiness; d. none of the above. (pp. 10-11)

19. ___ theorists take the position that sex and love are means to self-actualization. a. social learning; b. psychoanalytic; c. sociological; *d. humanistic; e. all of the above. (p. 12)

20. Almost all societies: a. regulate sexual behavior; b. condemn incest; c. condemn forced sexual relations; d. both b & c; *e. all of the above. (pp. 15, 18)

21. It is commonly believed by the ___ that menopause can produce insanity. a. mid-Americans; b. Mangaians; *c. people of Inis Beag; d. So; e. majority of preliterate cultures. (p. 16)

22. The society of Inis Beag is described as being one: *a. of the most naive and sexually repressive societies in the world; b. in which sex for pleasure and procreation is a principal interest; c. employing polygyny to deal with the greater number of women than men; d. employing polyandry to deal with the greater number of men than women; e. none of the above. (p. 16)

23. Specific instruction on sexual performance including oral sex, techniques for simultaneous orgasm, etc., is given to pubescent: a. mid-Americans; *b. Mangaians; c. Kerakians; d. Inis Beagians. (p. 17)

24. The use of pain for arousal is a part of the sexual technique of a number of societies: a. and it is commonly the man who inflicts pain on the woman; *b. and it is commonly the woman who inflicts pain on the man; c. although it is only practiced by deviate members of the society; d. but has not been recorded among non-Western, preliterate societies. (p. 18)

25. Adult masturbation: a. is found only in modern societies; b. is disapproved of by almost all human societies; c. appears to be practiced by some people in all societies; d. both a & b; *e. both b & c. (pp. 18-19)

26. In their cross-cultural examination of homosexuality, Ford & Beach reached several conclusions. Which of these is NOT one of them? a. no matter how a particular society treats it, homosexuality always occurs in at least some individuals; b. males are more likely to engage in homosexual behavior than are females; c. homosexual behavior is never the predominant form of sexual behavior for adults; *d. homosexuality is nonexistent in approximately 1/3 of human societies. (p. 19)

27. Our society's standards of physical attractiveness are in the minority in that we are more likely to: a. judge attractiveness by the appearance of the external genitals; b. accord importance to the shape and color of eyes; c. find plumpness attractive; *d. find thinness attractive; e. like dirt. (p. 20)

28. In our own culture, upper and middle-class couples, as compared with lower-class couples, are less likely to: a. sleep in the nude; b. use a variety of positions in intercourse; *c. have sex in total darkness; d. engage in oral sex. (p. 21)

29. As we move along the range from lower species (fish, rodents) to humans, the tendency is for sexual behavior to be more influenced by: a. instincts; b. hormones; *c. learning; d. drives. (p. 25)

30. Masturbation, oral-genital stimulation, and homosexuality have: a. not been observed among species other than humans; b. been observed in male but not female animals; c. been observed in female but not male animals; *d. been observed among both male and female animals. (pp. 23-25)

True/False

1. For Hyde, "sex" includes gender, sexual behavior, and sexual anatomy and physiology (F, p. 3).

2. Sperm were first discovered swimming in human semen during the early 20th century (F, p. 4).

3. According to contemporary scientists, a vaginal orgasm is more mature than a clitoral orgasm (F, p. 8).

4. Freud overemphasized the biological determinants of behavior, according to many modern psychologists (T, pp. 8-9).

5. The treatment of child molesters with aversion therapy stems from motivation theory (F, p. 11).

6. According to transactional analysis, when we feel aroused by someone, it is the "child" in us reacting (T, p. 12).

7. Ford and Beach (1951) reviewed the sexual behavior of almost 200 societies and concluded that our culture was sexually "restrictive" (T, p. 15).

8. Mangaian parents encourage their daughters to have sexual experiences with several men so that they may find a congenial marriage partner (T, p. 17).

9. There are no societies in which kissing is unknown (F, p. 18).

10. The lowest average frequency of intercourse for married couples cross-culturally appears to be about once every 2 months (F, p. 18).

11. Relative to other cultures, the frequency with which Americans have sex appears to be rather low (T, p. 18).

12. Cross-cultural studies indicate that gender roles in sexuality (who should initiate, etc.) vary tremendously from one society to the next (T, p. 20).

13. Blacks tend to have less of a double standard about sex than do whites (T, p. 22).

14. Cross-cultural research has demonstrated great variability in sexual behavior, suggesting that the manner in which human sexuality is expressed is strongly influenced by the culture in which we are raised (T, p. 22).

15. Observations of other species suggest that mammals are basically bisexual (T, p. 23).

16. Humans appear to be the only species to use sex for nonsexual purposes (F, p. 26).

Matching

Match the researcher on the right with the kind of research he, she, or they conducted.

____1. Large survey of sexual behavior in 1940's.

____2. Physiology of sexual response.

____3. Anthropological studies of sex.

____4. Early studies of "deviant" sexual behavior.

a. Masters & Johnson

b. Mead

c. Kinsey

d. Krafft-Ebing

e. Jorgenson

CHAPTER 2: SEXUAL ANATOMY

I. LEARNING OBJECTIVES

Study of this chapter should enable the student to:

1. Describe the similarities and differences between the clitoris and the penis.

2. Compare the various arguments given for clitoroidectomy and circumcision.

3. Compare the structure and function of the female and male external genitalia. What is one of the major differences between the two?

4. Briefly trace the history of phallic worship.

5. Compare the male and female internal sexual organs and glands and be able to indicate where they are located in a diagram of the body.

6. Describe the structure of breasts.

7. Indicate the procedures and purposes of a pelvic examination.

8. Be aware of methods of increasing the chances of producing a child of the gender of your choice.

9. Indicate the findings on which Shettles' procedures are based.

10. Examine the common anxieties associated with male sexual anatomy and with female sexual anatomy and indicate the extent to which each of these anxieties is realistic.

11. Describe the path and processes involved in the voyages of the egg from the uterus and of the sperm from the testis.

12. Describe the development of sperm.

13. Define the anatomical terms associated with the male and female reproductive organs.

II. CHAPTER AT A GLANCE

Introduction (p. 30)

Female Sexual Organs (pp. 30-40)
External Organs: Defines vulva.
The clitoris: Describes the organ, defines homologous and notes similarity of clitoris to penis. Also notes unique aspects of clitoris and gives brief history of clitoroidectomy.
The mons: Described.
The labia: Described and located.
Bartholin's glands: Described and located.
What you see is what you get: Notes that male external genitals are much more visible than female external genitals.
The hymen: Described, plus historical background on significance attached to intact hymen, notes that it is not a reliable indicator of virginity or sexual experience.
Internal Organs
The vagina: Structure and function; walls and location of nerve supply are described, debunks concern with size of vagina. Describes pubococcygeal muscle and discusses myths regarding the vagina as a trap.
The uterus: Structure and function, and describes the three layers and their part in menstruation and childbirth.
The fallopian tubes: Structure and function in fertilization.
The ovaries: Structure and function and describes follicles and egg releasing process.
The Breasts: Structure and function, plus discussion of concern with breast size and shape.
The Pelvic Exam: Describes the importance of the exam and details of the procedure.

Male Sexual Organs (pp. 40-47)
The Penis: Structure and function, engorgement process, discussion of various myths regarding penis muscles and bones, and various rationales for circumcision. Debunks myths regarding circumcision and briefly notes history of phallic worship. Discusses concern with penis size and castration anxiety.
The Scrotum and Testes: Structure and function in sperm and hormone production. Discusses way mumps may produce sterility, the movement of scrotum and testes in response to variations in temperature and emotion, and the effects of temperature on fertility.
Sperm: Development, structure and function. Discusses chromosomes and the fertilization process and describes Shettles' work with gender determination, giving details of the procedures. Describes the voyage taken by the sperm.
Other Internal Structures: Describes seminal vesicles, prostate, Cowper's glands and how their secretions may result in impregnation of a woman when a man has not ejaculated.

Summary (pp. 47-48)

Suggestions for Further Reading (p. 48)

III. GLOSSARY

areola. The dark area of skin surrounding the nipple of the breast.

Bartholin's glands. Two tiny glands located on either side of the vaginal entrance.

bulbourethral glands. See Cowper's glands.

cervix. The lower part of the uterus; the part next to the vagina.

circumcision. The surgical removal of the foreskin of the penis.

clitoris. A small, highly sensitive sexual organ in the female, located in front of the vaginal entrance.

corona. The rim of tissue between the glans and the shaft of the penis.

corpora cavernosa. Two cylindrical masses of erectile tissue running the length of the penis; also present in the clitoris.

corpus spongiosum. A cylinder of erectile tissue running the length of the penis.

Cowper's glands. A pair of glands that secrete substances into the male's urethra.

cremaster muscle. A muscle in the scrotum.

endometrium. The inner lining of the uterus.

epididymis. Highly coiled tubules located on the edge of the testis; the site of sperm maturation.

erection. An enlargement and hardening of the penis which occurs during sexual arousal.

fallopian tube. The tube extending from the uterus to the ovary.

follicle. The capsule of cells surrounding an egg in the ovary.

foreskin. The sheath of skin covering the tip of the penis or clitoris.

19

genitals. The sexual or reproductive organs.

glans. The tip of the penis or clitoris.

homologous organs. Organs in the male and female that develop from the same embryonic tissue.

hymen. A membrane that partially covers the vaginal opening.

inner lips. Thin folds of skin on either side of the vaginal entrance.

interstitial cells. Cells in the testes which manufacture male sex hormones; also called Leydig cells.

labia majora. See outer lips.

labia minora. See inner lips.

Leydig cells. See interstitial cells.

mons pubis. The fatty pad of tissue under the pubic hair; also called the mons or mons veneris.

outer lips. The fatty pads of tissue lying on either side of the vaginal opening and inner lips.

ovaries. The paired sex glands in the female which produce ova (eggs) and sex hormones.

oviduct. Fallopian tube.

ovulation. Release of an egg by the ovaries.

penis. A male sexual organ.

perineum. The area between the vaginal opening and the anus.

phallus. Penis.

phimosis. A condition in which the foreskin is so tight that it cannot be retracted.

prepuce. Foreskin.

prostate. The gland in the male, located below the bladder, that secretes most of the fluid in semen.

pubococcygeal muscle. The muscle around the vaginal entrance.

pudendum. The external genitals of the female.

scrotum. The pouch of skin that contains the testes.

semen. The fluid that is ejaculated from the penis during orgasm; it contains sperm.

seminal vesicles. The two organs lying on either side of the prostate.

seminiferous tubules. Highly coiled tubules in the testes that manufacture sperm.

smegma. A cheesy substance formed under the foreskin of the penis.

spermatogenesis. The production of sperm.

testes. The sex glands of the male, located in the scrotum; they manufacture sperm and sex hormones.

tumescence. Swelling due to congestion with body fluids.

urethra. The tube through which urine leaves the bladder and passes out of the body; in males, also the tube through which semen is discharged.

uterus. The organ in the female in which the fetus develops.

vagina. The barrel-shaped organ in the female into which the penis is inserted during intercourse and through which a baby passes during birth.

vas deferens. The ducts through which sperm pass on their way from the testes to the urethra.

virgin. A girl or woman who has never had sexual intercourse.

vulva. The collective term for the external genitals of the female; includes the mons, the clitoris, the inner and outer lips, and the vaginal and urethral openings.

IV. AUDIO-VISUAL AIDS

Movies:

Near the big chakra. Multi Media, #345, 15 min., color, silent, $175/$30. Exploration of a variety of vulvas of 38 women ranging in age from 6 months to 56 years.

<u>Tapes</u>:

<u>The body</u>. Norton, #340031, 60 min., $13.75. Detailed description
of male and female internal and external sexual and reproductive anatomy. Explores sexual concerns and myths regarding
circumcision, erection, vocabulary, breasts, cryptorchidism,
the clitoris, and the hymen.

V. DEMONSTRATIONS OR GROUP DISCUSSION

A. <u>Anatomical anxieties</u>: Distribute sheets of paper to students
during the class session before you begin Sexual Anatomy. Point out
that many of us worry about various parts of our anatomy in terms of
size, shape, smell, etc., although many of these anxieties have
little basis in fact. Ask them to indicate their gender (but not
their name) and to list all of the anxieties about sexual functioning and structure that they have experienced. Suggest that they put
a little asterisk by each one that is still of concern. Have <u>every-
one</u> return a folded sheet of paper with something written on it (at
the very least, they can list the common anxieties and then indicate
that they have not worried about any of them, personally). The purpose of this, of course, is to ensure that those who do have some
concerns will feel free to write them down since everyone else will
be writing. Collect and tabulate the sheets so that you may provide
feedback about the proportion of males worrying about penis size,
females worrying about breast size, etc., when you discuss sexual
anatomy. This information may be presented while doing the next
demonstration.

B. <u>Sexual anatomy</u>: This chapter (and the next on hormones and
sexual differentiation) contains fairly difficult material from the
standpoint of the ease with which students assimilate it; thus the
use of audio-visual aids is very helpful. The Unitarian Universal-
ists Association kit, "About your sexuality," contains some good
filmstrips for use in describing anatomy, including a variety of
pictures of hymen shapes and penis shapes. See the list of film
distributors at the end of the book for a description of the kit.

C. <u>Anatomy drawing</u>: This exercise helps students test their own
knowledge of sexual anatomy and stimulates them to ask questions.
Split the class into small groups of 6-8 students. Each group
should have 2 sheets of paper. Ask each group to make 2 drawings,
one of the male sexual/reproductive anatomy, one of the female, each
from a side view. On the drawings, they should label the following
parts. <u>Male</u>: penis, urethra, corpus spongiosum, corpora cavernosa,
urinary bladder, testes, scrotum, epididymis, vas deferens, prostate,
seminal vesicles, Cowper's gland. <u>Female</u>: vagina, uterus, fallopian
tubes, ovaries, clitoris, labia, urethra, urinary bladder, Bartholin's glands, cervix. When the students have finished, each group
should make a list of questions they have thought of while doing the

exercise. The rest of the class can be a question-and-answer session. Students can check the accuracy of their drawings against the text on p. 35 (female) and p. 41 (male).

D. Synonyms: This exercise furthers desensitization at the beginning of the course, as well as increasing students' vocabularies. The exercise can be done either in a large group or in small groups of 6-8. The instructor gives a scientific sexual term. Students must say as many synonyms for it as they can, as quickly as possible with a volunteer recording the list. Terms that can be used include the following: penis, intercourse, clitoris, masturbation, and orgasm.

VI. EVALUATION MATERIALS

Essay or research questions

1. Your cousin is planning to marry next month. She's been raised with very little in the way of sex education and has not had pre-marital intercourse. She knows you've had a course on sexuality and approaches you for information about a variety of concerns about breast size, her vagina, hymen, etc. What would you tell her? (See pp. 33-34 on the hymen, pp. 34-36 on the vagina, and pp. 38-39 on breasts.) Your students may want to follow up the issue of the kind of information which is available to young people in the community by (1) checking with the public schools to see who teaches sex education and what is included in their syllabi; and (2) checking with the community library to see if up-to-date information is available. They should also note whether sex books are on the shelves or if the patron has to ask the librarian specifically to see sex education books. This project would also be appropriate when the class is covering sex education (Chapter 22).

2. Describe the procedures involved in a pelvic exam and the purposes for each of the procedures. (See pp. 39-40 for a description. Female students may wish to write reports on their experiences with pelvic exams with respect to the extent to which the procedures described in the book are actually used by their doctors for anonymous presentation to the class.)

3. Describe the procedures that Shettles recommends for the couple wishing to conceive a girl (boy). (See pp. 46-47.)

Multiple choice

1. Recently, a trend has emerged: a. away from the view that only physicians should understand the functioning of the body; b. toward a view that everyone needs more information about his or her own body; c. toward a view that physicians alone have the

necessary background to understand the functioning of the body;
*d. both a & b. (p. 30)

2. The vulva includes the inner and outer lips and: a. the mons
    pubis; b. the mons pubis and clitoris; *c. the mons pubis,
    clitoris, and vaginal opening; d. the mons pubis, clitoris,
    vaginal opening, and the vagina; e. all of the above, plus the
    uterus. (p. 30)

3. The clitoris is very similar to the penis, but it is NOT true
    that each: a. develops from the same embryonic tissue; *b. has
    direct functions in reproduction; c. has a glans and a shaft;
    d. is erectile; e. is the principle organ in producing sexual
    arousal. (p. 31)

4. The most visible part of the female sexual organs is (are) the:
    *a. mons pubis; b. outer lips; c. inner lips; d. labia majora.
    (p. 32)

5. The area of skin between the vaginal opening and the anus is
    called the: a. introitus; b. fourchette; *c. perineum;
    d. urethra. (p. 32)

6. The hymen: a. produces lubrication during sexual arousal;
    b. even when intact, generally has some openings in it; c. is
    absent at birth in some females; d. if absent, indicates that a
    woman is sexually experienced; *e. both b & c. (pp. 33-34)

7. The walls of the uterus have three layers. The ___ layer is
    muscular. a. inner; *b. middle; c. outer; d. inner and outer.
    (p. 37)

8. Beyond middle age, the walls of the vagina tend to: a. become
    thicker and more flexible; *b. become thinner and less flexible;
    c. produce more lubrication; d. none of the above. (p. 34)

9. Vaginismus is: a. a vaginal infection; b. lubricating fluid;
    *c. the involuntary tightening of the muscles around the introi-
    tus; d. the name for orgasmic contractions. (p. 36)

10. The endometrium of the uterus: *a. is richly supplied with
    glands and blood vessels; b. is made of muscle; c. creates the
    strong contractions of childbirth; d. all of the above. (p. 37)

11. During menstruation, it is the ___ which is sloughed off and
    creates most of the menstrual discharge; a. perimetrium;
    b. myometrium; *c. endometrium; d. none of the above. (p. 37)

12. Fertilization of the egg by the sperm typically occurs in the
    a. vagina; b. uterus; *c. fallopian tube; d. ovary. (p. 38)

13. Each ovary is about the size of: a. a fist; *b. an unshelled almond; c. a baseball; d. the head of a pin. (p. 38)

14. The ovaries: a. produce eggs; b. manufacture female sex hormones; c. receive the sperm for fertilization; d. all of the above; *e. both a & b. (p. 38)

15. Females: *a. are born with about 400,000 immature eggs; b. are born without eggs, but begin to produce them at puberty; c. have fallopian tubes which are directly connected to the ovaries; d. none of the above. (p. 38)

16. In a pelvic exam, there is a test for stress incontinence in which: a. the internal organs are inspected; *b. the patient is asked to cough to see if urine flows involuntarily; c. a speculum is inserted into the vagina; d. the doctor's finger is inserted into the rectum. (p. 39)

17. The raised ridge separating the glans from the shaft of the penis is called the: a. glans; b. meatus; *c. corona; d. corpora cavernosa. (p. 40)

18. The human penis contains: *a. space-filled tissues which fill with blood during sexual arousal; b. a number of muscles, some of which are involved in erection; c. a small bone which can be felt only when the penis is flaccid or unaroused; d. both a & b. (p. 40)

19. Data collected on the relationship between circumcision and cancer: a. indicate that circumcision causes reduced risk of cancer; b. indicate that lack of circumcision causes an increased risk of cancer; *c. do not permit us to conclude that circumcision causes a reduced risk of cancer; d. have not yet been collected. (p. 42)

20. The circumcized male, as compared with the uncircumcized male: *a. receives more pleasure because the glans is exposed and receives more stimulation; b. receives less pleasure because the absence of a foreskin makes the glans become desensitized from constant stimulation; *c. does not differ in excitability. (p. 43)

21. The testes are analogous to the female's: a. uterus; b. vagina; c. breasts; *d. ovaries. (p. 44)

22. The ___ manufacture sperm. a. interstitial cells; b. seminal vesicles; c. Cowper's glands; *d. seminiferous tubules; e. none of the above. (p. 44)

23. The ___ produce testosterone. *a. interstitial cells; b. tunica albuginea; c. dartos muscle; d. seminal vesicles. (p. 44)

24. The ___ encapsulates the testis and divides it into sections.
a. interstitial cells; b. dartos muscles; *c. tunica albuginea;
d. seminal vesicles. (p. 45)

25. Shettles claims that X-bearing sperm, compared with Y-bearing
sperm: a. have smaller heads; b. are lighter; c. move faster;
*d. survive better. (p. 46)

26. The ___ may store sperm while they mature for as long as six
weeks. a. interstitial cells; b. seminiferous tubules; c. vas
deferens; *d. epididymis. (p. 47)

27. The prostate: a. is composed of muscle; b. is composed of glandular tissue; c. secretes an alkaline, milky fluid which com-
poses the major portion of the semen; *d. all of the above;
e. b & c only. (p. 47)

28. Sperm do not appear to be capable of movement on their own until
they: a. reach the epididymis; b. reach the vas; *c. mix with
the secretions of the prostate and seminal vesicles; d. reach
the urethra; e. reach the vagina. (p. 47)

29. A woman may become pregnant from the sperm in the fluid from the
___ even though the man has not ejaculated. a. seminal vesicles;
b. prostate; *c. Cowper's gland; d. epididymis. (p. 47)

True/False

1. A woman's urine passes out through her vagina (F, p. 30).

2. A woman's urine passes out through her clitoris (F, p. 30).

3. The inner lips are part of a woman's internal genitals (F, p. 30).

4. All parts of the female sexual anatomy serve dual sexual-repro-
ductive functions (F, p. 31).

5. Clitoroidectomies have been performed in the Middle East, Africa,
and Latin America, but have never been performed in the United
States (F, p. 32).

6. The nerve supply of the vagina is mostly in the outer third, near
the introitus (T, p. 34).

7. Small breasts are probably more erotically sensitive per square
inch than large breasts (T, p. 39).

8. During a pelvic exam, a doctor may place one finger into the
vagina and one into the rectum to get information on the positioning of the pelvic organs (T, p. 39).

9. A small penis tends to grow more in erection than a large penis (T, p. 43).

10. The testes are considered part of the internal genitals (T, p. 44).

11. The dartos muscle is located in the penis and aids erection (F, p. 45).

12. Spermatogenesis occurs continuously in the adult human male (T, p. 45).

13. The average male produces about 25 million sperm in his lifetime (F, p. 46).

14. A normal sperm carries 46 chromosomes in its tail (F, p. 46).

15. An egg may contain either an X chromosome or a Y chromosome (F, p. 46).

16. According to Shettles, more males than females are conceived (T, p. 47).

17. The prostate is fairly small at birth, enlarges at puberty, and typically shrinks in old age (T, p. 47).

Matching

Using the diagram of the male on the next page, match each of the following terms with its location:

Location		Terms
1. ___	9. ___	a. vas deferens
		b. bladder
2. ___	10. ___	c. pubic bone
		d. testis
3. ___	11. ___	e. scrotum
		f. Cowper's gland
4. ___	12. ___	g. rectum
		h. seminal vesicle
5. ___	13. ___	i. corpora cavernosa
		j. glans
6. ___	14. ___	k. epididymis
		l. prostate
7. ___	15. ___	m. urethra
		n. corpus spongiosum
8. ___		o. seminiferous tubules

Using the diagram of the female on the next page, match each of the following terms with its location:

Location		Terms
1. ___	7. ___	a. bladder
		b. vagina
2. ___	8. ___	c. inner lips
		d. cervix
3. ___	9. ___	e. ovary
		f. anus
4. ___	10. ___	g. fallopian tube
		h. clitoris
5. ___	11. ___	i. uterus
		j. urethra
6. ___		k. outer lips

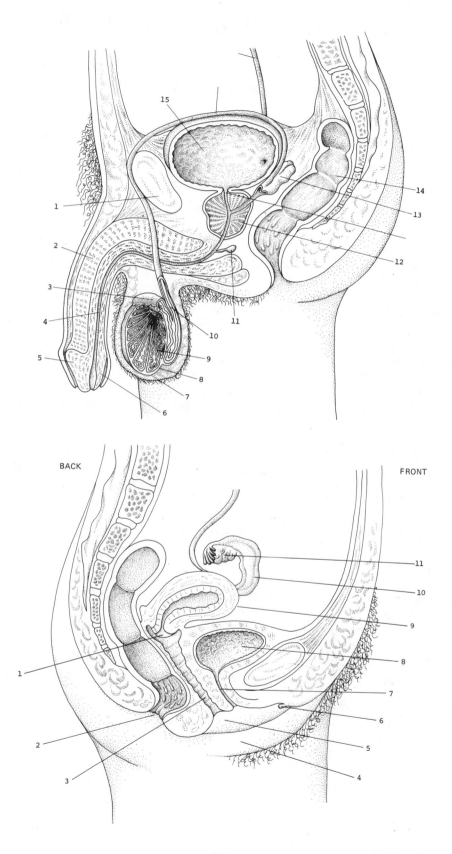

BACK

FRONT

CHAPTER 3: SEX HORMONES AND SEXUAL DIFFERENTIATION

I. LEARNING OBJECTIVES

Study of this chapter should enable the student to:

1. Specify the source and function of each of the hormones important for sexuality.

2. Describe the negative feedback loop regulating sex hormone levels in the male and in the female.

3. Compare and contrast the male and female sex hormone systems.

4. Specify when and how sexual differentiation begins in the embryo and describe the differences in the process for the male and female.

5. Describe sex differences in the brain in terms of their location and their effect.

6. List the eight variables of gender, and indicate their relationship to normal and abnormal gender development.

7. Describe the homologous and analogous sex organs in males and females.

8. Specify the evidence that exists to support the hypothesis that gender identity is a result of learning vs. that which exists to suggest that gender identity is largely due to "biological programming."

9. Indicate the difference between puberty and adolescence.

10. Describe the process of puberty in the male and in the female from the standpoint of changes in external appearance, internal functioning, and hormonal and glandular activity.

11. Describe some of the potential problems associated with puberty.

12. Evaluate the contributions John Money has made to our understanding of the process of sexual differentiation.

13. Define and describe hermaphroditism, adrenogenital syndrome, progestin-induced hermaphroditism, and testicular feminizing syndrome.

II. CHAPTER AT A GLANCE

<u>Introduction</u>: Notes that both the male and female develop from a
single cell, the fertilized egg.

<u>Sex Hormones</u> (pp. 50-53): Testosterone, estrogen, and progesterone
are considered, along with their relationship to the pituitary,
hypothalamus, and gonads.
  <u>Sex Hormone Systems in the Male</u>: Describes production and effects
    of testosterone on development of secondary sex characteris-
    tics. Discusses effects of FSH and LH, and the negative feed-
    back loop. Notes that testosterone level in males is fairly
    constant.
  <u>Sex Hormone Systems in the Female</u>: Describes functions of estro-
    gen and progesterone in development, and their fluctuation
    during the menstrual cycle. Notes the roles of FSH and LH and
    the negative feedback loop. Introduces prolactin. Notes that
    female hormone system is more complex than the male system in
    two ways.

<u>Prenatal Sexual Differentiation</u> (pp. 53-56)
  <u>Sex Chromosomes</u>: Describes normal and abnormal gender determina-
    tion, cell division up to 6th week, post-conception.
  <u>Gonads</u>: Describes the beginning of sexual differentiation at 7th
    week, plus speculation as to what causes the process.
  <u>Hormones and the Internal and External Genitals</u>: Notes degenera-
    tion of Wolffian ducts (female) and development of Mullerian
    ducts into female sex organs and the reverse process in males.
    Describes speculation about the responsible mechanisms, and
    notes that 4 months, post-conception, fetal gender is clear
    from appearance of external genitals.
  <u>Descent of the Testes and Ovaries</u>: Describes the process and
    several problems that may occur during the process.
  <u>Brain Differentiation</u>: Describes the impact of presence or
    absence of testosterone on development of gender differences
    in the hypothalamus, and the consequences of this differentia-
    tion for cyclicity. Notes the possibility of effects on
    aggressive and sexual behavior.
  <u>Homologous Organs</u>: Defines homologous and analogous.

<u>John Money, Hermaphrodites and the Eight Variables of Gender</u> (pp. 56-
  59): Describes distinctions between the eight variables of gender
  (see pp. 6-7) and notes that inconsistencies between the variables
  can result in a variety of "accidents" including pseudohermaphro-
  dites, the adrenogenital syndrome, progestin-induced hermaphroditism, and testicular feminizing syndrome. Describes Money's
  findings from research with individuals having these variations
  and notes the implications for gender determination complexity and
  the nature/nurture debate. Brief discussion of gender reassignment, including critique of Money's conclusions.

<u>Puberty</u> (pp. 59-67): Defines the term and distinguishes it from ado-
lescence; notes that its the second important period for sexual
differentiation and describes the variation in timing of puberty
among individuals and between males and females.
<u>Changes in the Female</u>: Describes average ages of various changes
of puberty and the roles played by hormones. Discusses cultural responses.
<u>Changes in the Male</u>: Same as for female, plus mention of capa-
city to ejaculate and have noctural emissions.

<u>Summary</u> (p. 67)

<u>Suggestions for Further Reading</u> (p. 68)

<u>Focus</u>:

<u>Two Case Histories from Johns Hopkins Clinic</u> (pp. 60-62)

III. GLOSSARY

<u>androgens</u>. "Male" sex hormones, produced in the testes; an
example is testosterone. In females, the adrenal glands
produce androgens.

<u>embryo</u>. In humans, the term used to refer to the unborn young
from the first to the eighth weeks after conception.

<u>endocrine gland</u>. A gland that secretes substances (hormones)
directly into the bloodstream.

<u>estrogen</u>. A group of "female" sex hormones; also produced in
smaller quantities in males.

<u>fertilization</u>. The union of sperm and egg, resulting in concep-
tion.

<u>follicle-stimulating hormone (FSH)</u>. A hormone secreted by the
pituitary; it stimulates follicle development in females and
sperm production in males.

<u>gender identity</u>. The psychological sense of one's own maleness
or femaleness.

<u>gonads</u>. The ovaries or testes.

<u>hermaphrodite</u>. A person with both male and female sex glands,
that is, both ovaries and testicular tissue.

<u>hypothalamus</u>. A part of the brain which is important in regulat-
ing certain body functions.

32

inguinal canal. In the male, the passageway from the abdomen to the scrotum through which the testes usually descend shortly before birth.

interstitial-cell-stimulating hormone (ICSH). A hormone manufactured by the pituitary that stimulates the interstitial cells of the testes to produce testerone; identical to the hormone LH in the female.

luteinizing hormone (LH). A hormone secreted by the pituitary. In females, it causes ovulation; called ICSH in males.

Mullerian ducts. In the embryo, a pair of ducts that eventually become part of the female reproductive system.

nocturnal emission. Involuntary orgasm and ejaculation while asleep.

pituitary gland. A gland located on the lower surface of the brain; it secretes several hormones important to sexual and reproductive functioning.

progesterone. A female sex hormone produced by the corpus luteum.

pseudohermaphrodite. An individual whose external genitals resemble one gender but whose gonads are those of the opposite gender.

secondary sex characteristics. The physical characteristics, other than the sex organs, that distinguish the male from the female; examples are the woman's breasts and the man's beard.

testosterone. A hormone secreted by the testes in the male; it maintains secondary sex characteristics.

Wolffian ducts. Embryonic ducts which form part of the male's reproductive system.

IV. AUDIO-VISUAL AIDS

Movies:

Achieving sexual maturity. Media Guild, 21 min., color, $315/$30. Very well done film covering physiology and anatomy from conception through adulthood. Gives good explanation of the feedback system between the brain and the gonads in their impact on hormones. Covers development from both biological and social standpoint. Intersperses live nude models and diagrams in a highly effective manner. Discusses masturbation and has

33

explicit footage showing males and females masturbating. Instructor may want to discuss student reactions to this after the film.

Tapes:

John W. Money--New Developments in sex research. Norton, 23 min., $14.00. Review of sex experiments and some future plans in this area.

V. DEMONSTRATIONS OR GROUP DISCUSSION

Since the material in this chapter is probably most difficult for students to assimilate, using the time for lecture to go over the material presented in the text is probably most helpful to students.

VI. EVALUATION MATERIALS

Essay or research questions

1. How does the negative feedback loop operate in the male to keep testosterone levels fairly constant? (See pp. 51-52 for explanation of feedback system.)

2. Describe the ways in which the sex hormone systems are more complex for one gender than for the other. (See p. 53 for comparison.)

3. Cite the bases on which Money's research has been critized. Do you agree with this criticism? Why or why not? (See p. 59 for evaluation of Money's research.)

4. What are the physiological consequences of gender differences in the brain? To what extent do these differences manifest themselves in observable differences in human behavior? (See pp. 55-56 for description of brain differentiation and speculations about gender differences in sexual and aggressive behavior. Students may wish to read the research on behavioral differences and can use Psychological Abstracts for leads on the latest findings by looking up "sex differences.")

Multiple choice

1. ___ is one of the androgens. *a. testosterone; b. estrogen; c. progesterone; d. none of the above. (p. 50)

2. Hormones: a. are secreted directly into the bloodstream;
    b. have effects that can occur fairly rapidly; c. can affect
    places in the body at quite a distance from where they are manu-
    factured; d. both a & b; *e. all of the above. (p. 50)

3. ___ is (are) important in regulating many vital behaviors in-
    cluding eating, drinking, and sexual behavior. a. the frontal
    lobe of the brain; *b. the hypothalamus; c. the adrenal gland;
    d. the ovaries and testes; e. none of the above. (p. 50)

4. Testosterone is produced in males by: a. the pituitary; b. the
    hypothalamus; *c. the testes; d. the pancreas. (p. 51)

5. Testosterone is maintained at a fairly constant level via a nega-
    tive feedback loop involving the: a. hypothalamus; b. hypothala-
    mus and pituitary; *c. hypothalamus, pituitary, and testes;
    d. hypothalamus, pituitary, testes, and medulla. (p. 51)

6. The menstrual cycle, pregnancy, pubertal changes, and sexual
    behavior are influenced by: a. the hypothalamus; b. the pitui-
    tary; c. the gonads (ovaries and testes); *d. all of the above;
    e. a & b only. (p. 51)

7. Testosterone: a. stimulates and maintains beard growth; b. main-
    tains the genitals; c. stimulates growth of bone and muscle;
    d. both a & b; *e. all of the above. (p. 51)

8. The pituitary produces: a. testosterone; b. FSH (follicle-
    stimulating hormone); c. LH (luteinizing hormone); *d. both b &
    c; e. all of the above. (p. 51)

9. Luteinizing hormone (LH) controls: *a. testosterone production;
    b. sperm production; c. both a & b; d. neither a nor b. (p. 51)

10. Estrogen: a. stops the growth of bones and muscles; b. stimu-
    lates breast growth; c. stimulates the growth of the uterus and
    vagina; d. both b & c; *e. all of the above. (p. 52)

11. The female sex hormone system functions similarly to the male
    system except: a. for the number of major hormones; b. the
    extent to which the hormones fluctuate; *c. both a & b;
    d. neither a nor b. (p. 53)

12. Differentiation of the gonads into testes or ovaries begins at
    about ___ after conception. a. a week; b. seven weeks;
    c. twelve weeks; *d. seven weeks for the male and twelve weeks
    for the female; e. twelve weeks for the male and seven weeks
    for the female. (p. 53)

13. Hyde suggests that it seems to be nature's basic plan to make a
    ___ and the addition of the ___ chromosome produces a variation,

the ___. *a. female, Y, male; b. female, X, male; c. male, Y, female; d. male, X, female. (p. 53)

14. In the prenatal differentiation process for the female, the ___ degenerate and the ___ turn into fallopian tubes, the uterus, and the upper part of the vagina. a. Mullerian ducts, Wolffian ducts; b. Mullerian ducts, tubercle; *c. Wolffian ducts, Mullerian ducts; d. Wolffian ducts, tubercle. (p. 55)

15. The scrotum develops from the: a. urethral primordia; b. Wolffian duct; c. Mullerian duct; *d. genital swelling. (p. 55)

16. The outer lips (labia majora) in women are homologous to the ___ in men. a. glans penis; b. epididymis; *c. scrotum; d. vas deferens; e. seminal vesicles. (p. 55)

17. Well documented differences in the brain have been found only in the: a. temporal lobe; b. cerebral cortex; *c. hypothalamus; d. cerebellum. (p. 55)

18. Ovaries and testes are: a. homologous; b. analogous; *c. both of the above; d. neither a nor b. (p. 56)

19. When a male organ and a female organ have similar functions, they are called: a. homologous; *b. analogous; c. both of the above; d. none of the above. (p. 56)

20. An important physiological consequence of gender differences in the brain may be seen: a. at puberty; b. in the cyclic secretion of sex hormones in the female; c. in the relatively constant production of sex hormones in the male; *d. all of the above; e. none of the above. (p. 56)

21. Sex differences in the brain produce well-documented differences in the ___ of men and women. a. sexual behavior; b. intelligence; c. altruistic behavior; d. all of the above; *e. none of the above. (p. 56)

22. The clitoris is analogous to the: a. testes; b. scrotum; c. prostate; *d. glans penis. (p. 56)

23. Of the eight variables of gender, ___ are ___. *a. 5, biological; b. 5, psychological; c. 2, chromosomal; d. 2, biological. (p. 57)

24. Hermaphroditism may be caused by: a. adrenogenital syndrome; b. giving progestin to pregnant women; c. testicular-feminizing syndrome; *d. all of the above; e. none of the above. (pp. 57-58)

25. With ___, the body tissues are insensitive to testosterone so that an individual is born with the external appearance of a female, with a vagina but no uterus, and undescended testes. a. adrenogenital syndrome; b. progestin-induced hermaphroditism; *c. testicular-feminizing syndrome; d. all of the above. (p. 58)

26. Money takes the position that gender identity is: a. biologically programmed; b. inherited; *c. learned; d. none of the above. (p. 58)

27. In general, gender reassignment is very successful up to the age of ___ but is very difficult beyond that age. a. six weeks; b. six months; *c. eighteen months; d. twelve years; e. eighteen years. (p. 59)

28. Major gender differences develop: a. at conception; b. after conception, but during the prenatal period; c. between birth and six months of age; d. during puberty; *e. both b & d. (p. 59)

29. Typically, girls begin to produce mature eggs: a. at birth; b. a year or two before menarche; c. at menarche; *d. a year or two after menarche. (p. 59)

30. Underarm hair begins to grow: a. before breast development; b. before pubic hair; c. at the same time as pubic hair; *d. about 2 years after pubic hair. (p. 63)

31. The ___, above the kidney, is the major producer of androgens in ___. a. pituitary, males; *b. adrenal gland, females; c. adrenal gland, males; d. liver, both sexes. (p. 64)

32. In girls, the major hormone influencing the development of pubic hair is: a. estrogen; b. progesterone; c. thyroxine; *d. adrenal androgen. (p. 64)

33. Temporary enlargement of the breasts occurs in about ___% of pubescent boys. a. 10; b. 25; c. 50; *d. 80; e. 100. (p. 67)

True/False

1. The process of sexual differentiation is completed by the time a child is born (F, p. 59).

2. The hypothalamus is important in regulating such behaviors as eating, drinking, and sex (T, p. 50).

3. The pituitary and the testes both produce hormones (T, p. 51).

4. The testes produce follicle-stimulating hormone (FSH) and luteinizing hormone (LH) (F, p. 51).

5. Follicle stimulating hormone (FSH) controls sperm production (T, p. 51).

6. Testosterone levels rise and fall in a monthly cycle in males (F, p. 51).

7. When testosterone levels are high, the hypothalamus reduces its production of LH-releasing factor (T, p. 52).

8. Prolactin stimulates milk secretion in women after they have given birth (T, pp. 52-53).

9. The male sex hormone system is more complex than the female sex hormone system (F, p. 53).

10. A fertilized egg with two X chromosomes will usually produce a male (F, p. 53).

11. Four months after conception, the embryo is still in a sexually undifferentiated state (F, p. 55).

12. The testes of the male do not begin to secrete androgens until puberty (F, p. 55).

13. Undescended testes are more likely to develop cancer (T, p. 55).

14. The testes must descend by puberty or the man will be sterile (T, p. 55).

15. Most of the research on the effects of sex differences in the brain on sexual and aggressive behavior has been done on animals (T, p. 56).

16. Girls produce mature ova earlier than boys produce mature sperm (F, p. 63).

17. When an organ in the male and an organ in the female both develop from the same embryonic tissue, the organs are analogous (F, p. 56).

18. In the female, the Mullerian duct degenerates, leaving only remnants (F, p. 56).

19. Assigned gender refers to a person's private, internal sense of maleness or femaleness (F, p. 57).

20. When there are contradictions among several of the biological variables of gender, the person is called an hermaphrodite (T, p. 57).

21. Puberty is the second important period for sexual differentiation (T, p. 59).

22. Hermaphroditism can result from giving a pregnant woman the drug progestin (T, p. 58).

23. The youngest mother on record was 5 years old (T, p. 63).

24. The average age of menarche is continuing to decline (F, p. 64).

25. The uterus doubles in size from the 10th to the 18th year (T, p. 64).

26. Females do not produce androgens (F, p. 64).

27. Orgasm and ejaculation are two separate processes although they generally occur together in adult males (T, p. 65).

28. A high voice will result from the castration of an adult male (F, p. 66).

29. The average age of voice change has declined over the last several centuries (T, p. 66).

30. Acne during puberty is more common in girls than in boys (F, p. 67).

Fill in the blank

Indicate which of the 8 variables of gender go with each definition.

1. ___: Estrogen and progesterone in the female; testosterone in the male.

2. ___: The announcement at birth, based on the appearance of the external genitals; the gender the parents and the rest of society believe the child to be; the gender in which the child is reared.

3. ___: XX in the female; XY in the male.

4. ___: Sexual attraction to members of the same gender, members of the opposite gender, or both.

5. ___: Ovaries in the female; testes in the male.

6. ___: Clitoris and vaginal opening in the female; penis and scrotum in the male.

7. ___: The person's private, internal sense of maleness or femaleness—which is expressed in personality and behavior—and the integration of this sense with the rest of the personality and with the gender roles prescribed by society.

8. ___: Uterus and vagina in the female; prostate and seminal vesicles in the male.

Answer key: 1. Hormonal gender; 2. Assigned gender; 3. Chromosomal gender; 4. Choice of sexual partner; 5. Gonadal gender; 6. External genital appearance; 7. Gender identity; 8. Internal accessory organs (p. 57).

CHAPTER 4:   MENSTRUATION AND MENOPAUSE

I. LEARNING OBJECTIVES

Study of this chapter should enable the student to:

1. Specify the differences between estrous cycles and menstrual cycles.

2. Describe the hormonal, ovarian, and uterine changes which occur with the phases of the menstrual cycle and indicate other cyclic changes.

3. Indicate the role of the corpus luteum in the menstrual cycle.

4. Know the amount and composition of menstrual fluid.

5. Describe the length of the various phases of the menstrual cycle and suggest how common a "regular" menstrual cycle is.

6. Define the terms Mittelschmertz, anovulatory cycle, dysmenor-rhea, endometriosis, and amenorrhea.

7. Describe the causes and symptoms of various menstrual problems.

8. Critically evaluate the research in support of the existence of a premenstrual syndrome.

9. Describe the evidence in support of or refuting the claim that women's "raging hormonal influences" render them unfit for the Presidency or similar important jobs.

10. Compare and contrast the nature/nurture explanations of mood fluctuations over the menstrual cycle.

11. Describe the extent to which we have evidence in support of the hypothesis that men also experience cyclicity.

12. Describe the causes of menopause in terms of its normal and problematic symptoms and its effect on sexuality.

13. Describe the changes that occur in middle-aged men.

14. Assess the contributions of Paige and Bart to this area.

Introduction (p. 70)

Biology and the Menstrual Cycle (pp. 70-76): Notes that humans are
    nearly unique among species in having a menstrual rather than
    estrus cycle and compares the two.
    The Phases of the Menstrual Cycle
        Hormones and what happens in the ovaries: Describes the
            follicular, ovulation, luteal, and menstruation phases.
        What happens in the uterus: Describes uterine changes during
            the four phases.
        Length and timing of the cycle: Describes the enormous varia-
            tion and the length of time for each of the phases, defines
            Mittelschmerz and anovulatory cycles.
        Other cyclic changes: Describes cervical mucus cycle and
            basal body temperature cycle and their use in determining
            time of ovulation.
    Menstrual Problems: Reviews dysmenorrhea (spasmodic and conges-
        tive) and household remedies for it, endometriosis, and pri-
        mary and secondary amenorrhea.

Psychological Aspects of the Menstrual Cycle (pp. 76-81)
    Fluctuations in Mood: Is Sally Blue? Describes symptoms of pre-
        menstrual tension, the premenstrual syndrome. Covers Bard-
        wick's research on mood and statistics on female crime and
        suicide. Reviews three ways in which the evidence on pre-
        menstrual syndrome has been criticized, and gives summary of
        conclusions.
    Fluctuations in Performance: Can Sally Be President? Briefly
        describes findings on work performance, concludes that there
        is no impairment. Reviews research suggesting peaks in sexual
        desire occur at ovulation and just prior to menstruation.
    Fluctuations in Sex Drive
    What Causes the Fluctuations in Mood: Why Is Sally Blue? Dis-
        cusses the biological (hormonal) vs. cultural explanations of
        mood fluctuations. Describes Paige's research on oral contra-
        ceptives and mood shifts. Reviews cross-cultural and relig-
        ious menstrual taboos, plus some contemporary research on sex
        during menstruation.

Cycles in Men (p. 82): Reviews the evidence on accidents and cycli-
    city, etc., but suggests paucity of research makes conclusions
    impossible.

Menopause (pp. 82-86)
    Biological Changes: Defines climacteric, describes hormonal and
        ovarian changes, physical symptoms, and their incidence in the
        population.
    Sexuality and Menopause: Describes changes in the vagina, and
        some positive and negative responses to menopause.

Psychological Changes: Describes psychological problems, involutional melancholia, but notes that adolescence may be more difficult than menopause.

What Causes the Symptoms: Reviews the evidence in support of biological (estrogen-deficient theory) vs. cultural or environmental explanations for menopausal symptoms. Covers Bart's "empty nest" research. Concludes with suggestions for biological and behavioral remedies.

Male Menopause (pp. 86-87)

Biological Changes: Notes gradual decline in testosterone and sperm production, and discusses prostate enlargement.

Psychological Changes: Describes "career crisis", difficulties in interaction with spouse who may be having her own problems.

Summary (pp. 87-88)

Suggestions for Further Reading (p. 88)

III. GLOSSARY

amenorrhea. The absence of menstruation.

climacteric. See menopause.

corpus luteum. The mass of cells remaining after a follicle has released an egg; it secretes progesterone.

dysmenorrhea. Painful menstruation.

edema. An excessive accumulation of fluid in a part of the body.

endometriosis. A condition in which the endometrium grows in some place other than the uterus, such as the fallopian tubes.

estrous. The period of ovulation and sexual activity in non-human female mammals.

menarche. The first menstruation.

menopause. The gradual cessation of menstruation in a woman, generally at around age 50.

menses. The menstrual flow.

menstruation. A bloody discharge of the lining of the uterus, generally occurring about once a month in women.

puberty. The period of time during which the body matures from that of a child to that of an adult capable of reproducing.

IV. AUDIO-VISUAL AIDS

Movies:

Achieving sexual maturity. This is described in Ch. 3, but may
be appropriately used here if it hasn't already been shown.

V. DEMONSTRATIONS OR GROUP DISCUSSION

Attitudes about menstruation: The purpose of this exercise is
to have students share some of the myths they have learned about
menstruation, and to clear up misunderstandings that may exist.
Begin by asking students to complete a worksheet with the following
instructions:

List as many synonyms as you can for "menstruation:"

When I was a kid, I heard _____ about menstruation.

    1._____

    2._____, etc.

After they have done this, have them indicate the source of
their "information" next to each of the items or synonyms. Then
divide the class into groups of 6-8. First, have them share their
lists of synonyms and make a complete list for the group. Next,
ask them to discuss each of the ideas about menstruation listed by
the group members. For each, the women in the group should tell
whether that idea is true, based on their own experience. Then ask
the group to discuss the scientific evidence and whether it backs
up each of the ideas. The instructor should serve as a resource
person at that point.

VI. EVALUATION MATERIALS

1. Describe several of the differences between estrous cycles and
menstrual cycles (p. 70).

2. Describe two changes during the menstrual cycle which may be
used to determine the time of ovulation (pp. 73-74).

3. What are three remedies for painful menstruation (p. 75)?

4. Critically evaluate the evidence in support of biological versus
cultural explanations for mood fluctuations associated with the
menstrual cycle. (See pp. 78-81; students may be directed to
"Menstruation" in Psychological Abstracts if they wish to write a
review of the latest findings on the topic.)

5. Compare male versus female biological and psychological changes that occur in middle-age. (See pp. 82-85 for women; pp. 86-87 for men.)

Multiple choice

1. The estrous phase of the estrous cycle: a. produces little or no bleeding; b. is when ovulation occurs; c. is the only time that the female is receptive to intercourse; d. both b & c; *e. all of the above. (p. 70)

2. Biologically, the last phase of the menstrual cycle is the ___ phase. a. follicular; b. ovulation; c. luteal; *d. menstruation. (p. 71)

3. Progesterone levels rise during the ___ phase. a. follicular; b. ovulation; *c. luteal; d. menstruation. (p. 71)

4. The pituitary secretes relatively high levels of FSH during the ___ phase of the menstrual cycle. *a. follicular; b. ovulation; c. luteal; d. menstruation. (p. 71)

5. There is a sharp decline in estrogen levels at the end of the ___ phase. a. follicular; b. ovulation; *c. luteal; d. menstruation. (p. 71)

6. Menstrual fluid is made of: a. blood; b. degenerated cells; c. mucus; *d. all of the above; e. a & b only. (p. 73)

7. A woman regularly has 40-day long menstrual cycles. She probably ovulates on: a. day 20; b. day 15; c. 14 days after her period is over; *d. day 26; e. 9 days after her period is over. (p. 73)

8. The corpus luteum produces: a. testosterone; *b. progesterone; c. menstrual fluid; d. mucus. (p. 73)

9. A menstrual period normally produces about ___ of fluid. a. 1 tablespoon; *b. 4 tablespoons; c. ½ cup; d. 1 cup. (p. 73)

10. In menstrual cycles that vary in length, it is the ___ phase which shows the most variation. *a. follicular; b. ovulation; c. luteal; d. menstrual. (p. 73)

11. The cervical mucus is most alkaline, thin, and watery just: a. after menstruation; b. a week before menstruation; c. a week after ovulation; *d. at ovulation. (p. 74)

12. An anovulatory cycle is a: a. male reproductive cycle; b. menstrual cycle including ovulation; c. cycle with two phases of ovulation; *d. cycle without ovulation. (p. 73)

13. A woman's basal body temperature is low: *a. on the day of ovulation; b. the day after ovulation; c. the day before menstruation; d. the day of menstruation. (p. 74)

14. This type of painful menstruation may get worse with each pregnancy: a. anovulation; b. spasmodic dysmenorrhea; *c. congestive dysmenorrhea; d. regressive dysmenorrhea. (p. 75)

15. Among the helpful remedies for painful menstruation are: a. aspirin; b. exercise; c. masturbation; d. both a & b; *e. all of the above. (p. 75)

16. The endometrium can grow in the: a. uterus; b. ovaries; c. bladder; *d. all of the above. (p. 75)

17. Amenorrhea is not caused by: a. pregnancy; b. emotional factors; c. cysts or tumors; d. hormonal imbalance; *e. premarital sex. (p. 76)

18. Mood fluctuations through the menstrual cycle appear to occur in ___ of women. a. 24% or less; b. 25-49%; *c. 50-75%; d. over 76%. (pp. 77-78)

19. Paige found that women with no mood shifts used ___ birth control pills. a. no; b. sequential; *c. combination; d. occasional. (p. 79)

20. Paige (1971) studied mood fluctuations in the menstrual cycle by: *a. measuring the mood levels of women who were taking birth control pills; b. administering estrogen to rhesus monkeys; c. asking women to engage in 3-day fasts; d. putting different hormones in pellets fed to female rats. (p. 79)

21. In Paige's study of the relationship between religious background and mood fluctuations, it was found that ___ women, on the average, showed no fluctuation. *a. Protestant; b. Catholic; c. Jewish; d. agnostic. (p. 81)

22. Hyde concluded that mood shifts during the menstrual cycle are probably caused by: a. biological (hormonal) factors; b. cultural factors; *c. various combinations of the above factors; d. none of the above. (p. 81)

23. Monthly cycles in men: a. have not been studied; b. do not exist; *c. have been observed in several studies; d. have been firmly established by research. (p. 82)

24. The major biological change during the climacteric is the:
a. reduction in FSH output; b. reduction in LH output;
*c. aging of the ovaries; d. increase in progesterone.
(p. 82)

25. During the climacteric, the pituitary responds to low levels of
estrogen and progesterone by: a. producing less FSH; b. producing less LH; *c. producing more FSH and LH; d. discontinuing
FSH and LH production. (pp. 82-83)

26. On the basis of the available research on the climacteric, Hyde
concluded that about ___ % of women appear to suffer severe
symptoms. *a. 10; b. 30; c. 60; d. 90. (p. 83)

27. With the decline in ___ during menopause, there is a decline in
vaginal lubrication during sexual arousal. *a. estrogen; b. progesterone; c. testosterone; d. all of the above. (p. 83)

28. Hyde concludes that the worst time in a woman's life, psychologically is: a. childhood; *b. adolescence; c. young adulthood;
d. menopause. (p. 85)

29. Bart's study of middle-aged women indicated that ___ have the
most depression. a. masculine women; b. career women; *c. traditional "supermothers"; d. married women. (pp. 85-86)

30. In addition to prescribing estrogen replacement to relieve
women's menopausal symptoms, Hyde suggests that ___ may be very
therapeutic. a. going back to school; b. developing a career;
c. volunteer work; *d. all of the above. (p. 86)

31. In middle age, men experience ___ decline in manufacture of both
testosterone and sperm. a. no; *b. a very gradual; c. a sudden;
d. a very dramatic. (p. 86)

32. Prostate enlargement during middle age: a. is extremely rare;
b. is caused by excessive sexual activity; *c. can be treated by
surgical removal of part of the gland; d. can be reduced by
administration of female sex hormones as long as the prostate
is not cancerous. (p. 86)

True/False

1. Human females are nearly unique among species in having a menstrual cycle (T, p. 70).

2. The menstrual cycle has two phases, each with its own hormonal,
ovarian, and uterine changes (F, p. 71).

3. During menstruation, estrogen and progesterone levels are high (F, p. 71).

4. The corpus luteum produces progesterone (T, p. 73).

5. Generally, if conception occurs, the fertilized egg arrives in the uterus about six days after ovulation (T, p. 73).

6. There is enormous variation from one woman to the next in the average length of the menstrual cycle (T, p. 73).

7. Progesterone lowers body temperature (F, p. 74).

8. Spasmodic dysmenorrhea is most common between the ages of 15 and 25 (T, p. 75).

9. Menstruation does not take place in an adult woman unless she has ovulated that month (F, p. 73).

10. For women with mood fluctuations during the menstrual cycle, mood is generally positive around the time of ovulation (T, p. 76).

11. Untreated endometriosis may lead to sterility (T, p. 76).

12. A large proportion of acts of violence and suicides committed by women occur during the eight premenstrual and menstrual days of the cycle (T, p. 77).

13. The available data suggest that women's work, athletic performance, etc., fluctuate with the phases of the menstrual cycle (F, p. 78).

14. In the 1970's, data were collected suggesting that intercourse during menstruation is rare (less than 10% of the population have ever done so) (F, p. 81).

15. Epileptic attacks appear to follow a monthly cycle in men (T, p. 82).

16. Virtually all women experience uncomfortable menopausal symptoms (F, p. 83).

17. Proponents of the "estrogen deficiency theory" argue that the physical symptoms of menopause are caused by declining amounts of estrogen in the body (T, p. 85).

18. Estrogen replacement therapy has not been very successful in relieving hot flashes, sweating, and vaginal discharge (F, p. 85).

19. Estrogen replacement therapy does not have any effect on psychological symptoms of menopause (F, p. 85).

20. Bart's study of middle-aged women suggested that loss of role is related to depression (T, pp. 85-86).

21. In cultures in which women's status increases with age, middle-aged women have a low depression rate (T, p. 86).

22. Enlargement of the prostate causes urination problems (T, p. 86).

23. Excessive masturbation and/or sexual activity is related to prostate enlargement in middle-aged men (F, p. 87).

24. Administration of female sex hormones reduces benign prostate enlargement (F, pp. 86-87).

25. The effects of venereal disease can include prostate enlargement (T, p. 87).

Matching

___ 1. Mittelschmerz

___ 2. anovulatory cycle

___ 3. dysmenorrhea

___ 4. endometriosis

___ 5. amenorrhea

a. absence of menstruation.

b. an infection of the endometrium.

c. a sensation, lasting for about a day, of cramping on one or both sides of the lower abdomen which occurs during ovulation for some women.

d. growth of the endometrium in some place other than the uterus.

e. painful menstruation.

f. menstrual cycle in which ovulation does not occur.

Matching answer key: 1. c; 2. f; 3. e; 4. d; 5. a.

CHAPTER 5: CONCEPTION, PREGNANCY, AND CHILDBIRTH

I. LEARNING OBJECTIVES

Study of this chapter should enable the student to:

1. Describe the independent voyages and first few days after connection of the sperm and ovum.

2. Trace the physical and psychological changes which occur in the mother and in the baby during each of the three trimesters.

3. Indicate the effects of different nutrients and drugs on the developing fetus at different stages of pregnancy.

4. Describe the sexual behavior of American women during pregnancy. What advice is given by contemporary physicians?

5. Describe the training for Lamaze (prepared) childbirth for the mother and father.

6. Describe the stages of labor.

7. Review the common anesthetics used in childbirth in terms of how and where they are given.

8. Describe the effects of anesthetics on the mother and baby and give the arguments for and against their use.

9. Understand the physical and psychological changes for the mother during the postpartum period.

10. Describe the biological and psychological processes involved in breastfeeding and indicate the advantages and disadvantages of breast- vs. bottle feeding for the mother and the infant.

11. Describe the causes and solutions of various problems of pregnancy.

12. Indicate the causes of infertility in the male, the female, and the couple.

13. Define the terms couvade, Hegar's sign, Nagele's rule, edema, effleurage, Lamaze method, ectopic pregnancy, pseudocyesis, amniocentesis, dilation, teratogenic, and episiotomy.

14. Describe the contributions of Dick-Read, Lamaze, and Masters & Johnson to our understanding of this area.

II. CHAPTER AT A GLANCE

<u>Introduction</u> (p. 90)

<u>Conception</u> (pp. 90-94)
<u>Sperm Meets Egg: The Incredible Journey</u>: Describes ovulation, intercourse, sperm, site of conception, cell division, and implantation. Gives terms for parts of the sperm and for fertilized egg at different stages of development.
<u>Improving the Chances of Conception: Making a Baby</u>: Describes use of basal body temperature chart, life span of sperm, coital positions, and douching.

<u>Development of the Conceptus</u> (pp. 94-98): Defines trimesters.
<u>The Embryo and its Support Systems</u>: Describes embryonic development, placenta, relationship of maternal and fetal circulatory systems, hormone production by the placenta, the umbilical cord, and amniotic fluid.
<u>Fetal Development During the First Trimester.</u>
<u>Fetal Development During the Second Trimester.</u>
<u>Fetal Development During the Third Trimester.</u>

<u>The Stages of Pregnancy</u> (pp. 98-104)
<u>The First Trimester (The First 12 Weeks)</u>
<u>Symptoms of pregnancy</u>: Describes missed period, breast symptoms, and "morning sickness."
<u>Pregnancy tests</u>: Reviews immunologic and biologic tests, the HCG radioimmunoassay, and the importance of early detection of pregnancy. Describes Hegar's sign and distinguishes between presumptive, probable, and positive signs of pregnancy. Gives the procedure for determining due date using Nagele's rule.
<u>Physical changes</u>: Notes hormonal and breast changes, increased urination, "morning sickness," vaginal discharge, and fatigue.
<u>Psychological changes</u>: Describes variability of changes, effect of a number of factors on pregnant woman's emotions.
<u>Couvade and sympathetic pregnancy</u>: Defines the terms, gives brief description.
<u>The Second Trimester (Weeks 13 to 26)</u>
<u>Physical changes</u>: Describes "quickening", edema, production of colostrum, increase in size of belly.
<u>Psychological changes</u>: Notes the relative calm of the period.
<u>The Third Trimester (Weeks 27 to 38)</u>
<u>Physical changes</u>: Describes increase in size of uterus, weight gain (and relative weights of infant, placenta, uterus, amniotic fluid, breasts, etc.). Briefly notes problems of excessive weight gain, defines Braxton-Hicks contractions and engagement.
<u>Psychological changes</u>: Describes increase in impatience, mild emotional disturbances, and the influence of maternal physical activity.

Sex During Pregnancy (pp. 104-105): Describes traditional prohibitions, Masters & Johnson's work on sex during pregnancy, and presents data on typical frequency patterns.

Nutrition (pp. 105-106): Reviews data on importance of maternal diet.

Effects of Drugs Taken During Pregnancy (pp. 106-108): Defines teratogenic, mentions thalidomide births.
Antibiotics
Addictive Drugs: Discusses alcohol, heroin, morphine, and methadone.
Steroids: Discusses synthetic hormones, excessive vitamins, DES.
Others: Discusses nicotine, antihistamines, x-rays, marijuana and LSD.

Birth (pp. 108-112)
The Beginning of Labor: Notes variation in signs (bloody show, membrane rupture, contractions) and the role of hormones in labor.
The Stages of Labor
First-stage labor: Defines effacement, dilation and transition.
Second-stage labor: Describes crowning and episiotomy (arguments pro and con) and birth.
Third-stage labor
Positions of the fetus: Describes cephalic, breech, and transverse.
Cesarean section (C section): Indicates reasons for C sections, describes procedure.

Natural Childbirth (pp. 112-114)
The Lamaze Method: Gives background, describes techniques of relaxation, controlled breathing, effleurage and the role of the father or coach.
The Use of Anesthetics in Childbirth: Gives historical overview, reviews some of the common anesthetics, and discusses various arguments for and against their use.

After the Baby is Born: The Postpartum Period (pp. 114-116)
Physical Changes: Briefly reviews role of hormones, notes exhaustion.
Psychological Changes: Describes postpartum depression, frequency of occurrence.

Breast-Feeding (pp 116-118)
Biological Mechanisms: Describes the roles of prolactin, oxytocin in milk production, colostrum secretion.
Psychological Aspects: Gives brief history, describes incidence, and notes advantages of breastfeeding. Describes role of La Leche League.

Problem Pregnancies (pp. 118-122)
    Ectopic Pregnancy: Describes incidence, symptoms and resolution.
    Pseudocyesis (False Pregnancy)
    Toxemia: Describes preclampsia and eclampsia, associated symp-
        toms, and association of toxemia with socioeconomic status.
    Illness During Pregnancy: Discusses influence of viruses using
        rubella as example, herpes simplex, flu, colds, and pneumonia.
    Defective Conceptus: Reviews incidence and some causes, des-
        cribes amniocentesis and conditions under which it should be
        performed.
    Rh Incompatibility: Describes associated problems and techniques
        for reducing them.
    Miscarriage (Spontaneous Abortion): Describes frequency and
        causes.
    Prematurity: Notes incidence, problems and factors associated
        with prematurity.

Infertility (pp. 122-123): Distinguishes infertility from sterility,
    notes incidence.
    Causes of Infertility
        Causes in the female
        Causes in the male
        Combined factors: Discusses immunologic responses, ignorance,
            reviews influence on marriage.
    Psychological Factors

Summary (pp. 123-124)

Suggestions for Further Reading (p. 124)

III. GLOSSARY

    amniotic fluid. The watery fluid surrounding a developing fetus
        in the uterus.

    blastocyst. A small mass of cells that results after several
        days of cell division by the fertilized egg.

    breech presentation. Presentation of the buttocks and/or feet
        first during birth.

    cesarean section. Surgical delivery of a baby through an inci-
        sion in the abdomen.

    colostrum. A watery substance that is secreted from the breast
        at the end of pregnancy and during the first few days after
        delivery.

    conceptus. The product of conception; sometimes used to refer
        to the embryo or fetus.

diethylstilbestrol (DES). A potent estrogen drug used in the "morning-after" pill.

douche. To flush out the inside of the vagina with a liquid.

ectopic pregnancy. A pregnancy in which the fertilized egg implants somewhere other than in the uterus.

episiotomy. An incision that is sometimes made at the vaginal entrance during delivery.

fetus. In humans, the term used to refer to the unborn young from the third month after conception until birth.

gametes. Sperm or eggs.

gestation. The period of pregnancy; the time from conception until birth.

human chorionic gonadotropin (HCG). A hormone that is produced by the placenta; HCG is what is detected in most pregnancy tests.

implantation. The burrowing of the fertilized egg into the lining of the uterus.

impregnate. To make pregnant.

labor. The series of processes involved in giving birth.

lactation. The secretion of milk from the female's breasts.

Lamaze method. A method of "prepared" childbirth.

lochia. A discharge from the uterus and vagina that occurs during the first few weeks after childbirth.

miscarriage. A pregnancy that terminates on its own; spontaneous abortion.

multiparous. A term used to refer to a woman who has had more than one baby.

nulliparous. A term used to refer to a woman who has never had a child.

oxytocin. A hormone secreted by the pituitary which stimulates the contractions of the uterus during childbirth; also involved in breast-feeding.

parturition. Childbirth.

placenta. An organ formed on the wall of the uterus through which the fetus receives oxygen and nutrients.

postpartum period. The period following childbirth.

prolactin. A hormone secreted by the pituitary; it is involved in lactation.

trimester. A period of three months.

umbilical cord. The tube that connects the fetus to the placenta.

IV. AUDIO-VISUAL AIDS

Movies:

Birth of a family. Perennial, #1051, 24 min., color, $300/$30. Interweaves childbirth preparation classes with actual delivery process. Very well done sequence of birth itself, showing reactions of mother, and discusses pain although mother doesn't demonstrate much pain. Husband participates in classes and birth process and film emphasizes importance of father participation. This is an explicit and excellent portrayal of prepared childbirth.

Labor of love: Childbirth without violence. Perennial, #1061, 27 min., color, $300/$30. Art Eulene narrates this film which describes the Leboyer method. Interviews Art Janov who connects his work on primal scream to importance of childbirth without violence. Contrasts a traditional delivery with a Leboyer delivery, but scenes of the Leboyer birth are difficult to see, since one of the aspects of Leboyer's method is dim lighting. Concludes with a series of pro and con statements from physicians representing various medical specialities.

Emotional aspects of pregnancy. Perennial, #1079, 23 min., color, $325/$32.50. This film was designed to prepare the expectant mother and father for the emotional changes of pregnancy. It highlights the experiences of two expectant couples and of one single expectant mother, and deals with changes in relationships, sexuality and dreams.

A baby is born. Perennial, #1015-79 (revised), 23 min., color, $300/$30. Film follows parents and doctor through the process of labor and birth. Portrays a long labor and deals with the purposes of episiotomy and the concerns and anxieties of the parents. The birth process itself is well filmed, although several students who previewed the film with one of the authors appropriately questioned the doctor's behavior and wondered how typical it was for a doctor to accompany the father into the locker room to change his clothes, etc. Has a post-natal visit (after a length of black film) in which the doctor talks about the process of birth spacing through contraceptive use.

Talking about breastfeeding. Polymorph, 17 min., color, $225/ $20. Interviews women who describe the effect of breastfeeding on them and their children. Discusses breastfeeding in the context of C-sections, premature delivery, pressure from relatives, sibling rivalry, and continuing a career.

Tapes:

In the beginning (getting pregnant). Norton, #340104, 60 min., $14. Begins with discussion between doctor and couple about their infertility problem. Discusses sperm and egg production, ejaculation, and menstruation. Concludes with discussion of adoption, fertility pills, artificial insemination, and the social concerns of being childless.

Pregnancy and birth. Norton, #340112, 60 min., $14. Discusses pregnancy, birth, and sexual concerns. Uses a pregnancy test to illustrate some of the emotions that surround first pregnancy. Describes fetal development, natural childbirth exercises, and breastfeeding techniques, and presents a live interview with a doctor and mother during a normal delivery.

V. DEMONSTRATIONS OR GROUP DISCUSSION

A. Lamaze lecture. Many communities now have Lamaze classes for couples who want to use prepared childbirth. Ask a Lamaze instructor (your hospital may be able to provide you with names) to speak to the class, and, if possible, to show the film The Story of Eric.

B. Leboyer lecture. Your local hospital may also be using this method and may be able to provide you with a speaker to come to the class and explain the method.

VI. EVALUATION MATERIALS

Essay or research questions

1. Describe the voyage of the sperm from the seminiferous tubules to their arrival in the fallopian tube. (See pp. 90-92.)

2. Give three reasons for the importance of early and accurate pregnancy detection. (See p. 100.)

3. Describe the potential effects of a pregnant woman's use of antibiotics or addictive drugs on the fetus. (See pp. 106-107; for

a research paper, you might suggest that students compare the material in their text with the latest research findings to indicate what antibiotics or drugs should be added or deleted.)

4. What physical and psychological changes in the woman are associated with each of the trimesters of pregnancy. (See pp. 101-104; students may want to interview several pregnant women to see the extent to which their experiences parallel those of the average woman.)

5. Compare and contrast the various methods of childbirth with respect to the roles taken by the mother and father, the use of anesthesia, etc. (See pp. 108-114; students may want to interview several women using different methods of childbirth to get their subjective responses to the different methods.)

6. Describe the advantages and disadvantages of breastfeeding for the mother and infant. What factors have accounted for the decline in breastfeeding in our culture? (See pp. 116-118; students might check the latest research on the incidence and effects of breastfeeding in our society.)

Multiple choice

1. After release from the ovary, the egg moves down the fallopian tube to the uterus: a. via self-propulsion in about one day; b. propelled by ovarian secretions in about two days; *c. propelled by cilia in about three days; d. propelled by gravity in about four days. (p. 90)

2. The sperm's chromosomal material is contained in the nucleus which is in the ___ of the sperm. *a. head; b. top of the body; c. bottom of the body; d. tail. (p. 91)

3. A typical ejaculate contains: a. 1500 sperm; b. 3,000 sperm; c. 5 million sperm; *d. 300 milion sperm. (p. 92)

4. Conception usually occurs in the: a. uterus; b. third of the fallopian tube nearest the uterus; *c. third of the fallopian tube nearest the ovary; d. ovary. (p. 92)

5. About ___ days after conception, the fertilized egg implants itself in the lining of the uterus. a. $1\frac{1}{2}$; b. 2-3; c. 3-4; *d. 5-7. (p. 92)

6. After ejaculation, it takes a man at least ___ to manufacture the number of sperm contained in an average ejaculate. a. 3 hours; b. 12 hours; *c. 24 hours; d. 48 hours. (p. 93)

7. If a woman wants to conceive, the best coital position is:
*a. on her back; b. "doggy" position (on her hands and knees
with her hips elevated); c. on the side from which she is ovu-
lating that month; d. on top of the man. (p. 93)

8. Among the substances which pass through the membrane barrier
between the mother's blood and baby's blood systems is (are):
a. oxygen; b. nutrients; c. syphilis spirochete; d. German
measles (rubella) virus; *e. all of the above. (pp. 94-95)

9. The umbilical cord is formed during the ___ of embryonic development. a. first day; b. first week; *c. fifth week; d. twelfth
week. (p. 95)

10. A baby born at the end of the ___ month has a 50% chance of survival. a. 5th; b. 6th; *c. 7th; d. 8th. (p. 97)

11. A woman's increased temperature after conception is due to high
levels of: a. estrogen; *b. progesterone; c. human chorionic
gonadotropin (HCG); d. chorionic somatomammotropin. (p. 99)

12. Using the most modern lab tests, the soonest that pregnancy can
be detected is: a. 2 days after conception; *b. 8 days after
conception; c. 3 days after a missed period; d. 8 days after a
missed period. (p. 100)

13. Positive signs of pregnancy are provided by: a. lab tests;
b. fetal heartbeat; c. fetal movement; *d. both b & c. (p. 101)

14. The breasts have completed their development in preparation for
nursing by the: a. middle of the first trimester; b. end of the
first trimester; *c. middle of the second trimester; d. middle
of the third trimester. (p. 103)

15. The largest source of weight gain in a pregnant woman is the
baby and the: a. placenta; b. amniotic fluid; c. enlargement
of breasts; *d. increased retention of fat and water; e. enlargement of uterus. (p. 103)

16. Generally, the best coital position for the very pregnant woman
is: a. "missionary"; b. woman above; *c. side-by-side; d. woman
sitting on man's lap. (p. 105)

17. The appropriate level of salt and calories during pregnancy:
*a. is currently a source of debate among physicians; b. is
low; c. is high; d. is low in salt and high in calories. (p.
106)

18. Drugs that produce birth defects are: a. detected using Hegar's
sign; b. called couvade; *c. called teratogenic; d. unknown.
(p. 107)

19. ___ is released by the pituitary and stimulates the last power-
ful contractions to push the fetus out. a. prostaglandins;
b. estrogen; *c. oxytocin; d. miraboxin. (p. 108)

20. A shoulder, arm, or hand emerges into the vagina in a ___ presentation. *a. transverse; b. breech; c. longitudinal;
d. reverse. (p. 110)

21. Which of the following is not true regarding cesarean sections?
a. recovery takes somewhat longer than normal birth; b. a woman
may have 2 or 3 cesareans; *c. the U.S. has the lowest percent
of cesareans of the Western industrialized countries; d. cesareans account for about 10% of U.S. deliveries. (p. 110)

22. ___ are the most commonly used anesthetic methods. *a. regional
anesthetics; b. general anesthetics; c. barbiturates; d. geo-
graphic anesthetics. (p. 114)

23. Historically, childbirth took place in the home with midwives.
This pattern began to change to use of physicians and hospitals
about ___ years ago. a. 500; *b. 300; c. 100; d. 50. (p. 113)

24. Use of anesthesia in childbirth has become routine since about
a. 1750: b. 1800; *c. 1850; d. 1900. (p. 113)

25. When the placenta is expelled, levels of: *a. estrogen and progesterone drop sharply; b. estrogen increase sharply; c. progesterone decrease sharply; d. estrogen and progesterone increase
sharply. (p. 114)

26. Mother's milk is produced beginning ___ delivery. a. about a
month before; b. about a week before; c. just at; *d. a few days
after. (p. 116)

27. Breast milk for a baby: a. contains ideal mixtures of nutrients;
b. contains protective antibodies; c. is bacteria free; d. is
always the right temperature; *e. all of the above. (p. 117)

28. Tubal pregnancy: a. occurs in about 1 out of every 2,000 pre-
nancies; b. is more likely in women of high socioeconomic
status; *c. is sometimes ended by spontaneous abortion; d. all
of the above. (p. 118)

29. Pregnancy complications can be caused by: a. rubella (German
measles); b. herpes virus; c. influenza; d. pneumonia; *e. all
of the above. (pp. 119-120)

30. Significant birth defects affect one family out of every: a. 3;
*b. 10; c. 25; d. 100. (p. 120)

31. Amniocentesis should be performed between the ___ and ___ week of pregnancy. a. 6th-8th; b. 10th-12th; *c. 14th-16th; d. 20th-22nd. (p. 120)

32. Amniocentesis generally should be performed when a pregnant woman: a. has already had one child with a genetic defect; b. believes that she's a carrier of a genetic defect; c. is over 40; d. both a & b; *e. all of the above. (p. 120)

33. Prematurity is assumed when the baby: a. is born 2 months early; *b. weighs less than $5\frac{1}{2}$ lbs.; c. weighs less than 6 lbs.; d. weighs less than $6\frac{1}{2}$ lbs. (p. 121)

34. Techniques for dealing with problems for the Rh- mother with an Rh+ baby include all but one of the following. Which is <u>not</u> a solution? a. giving fetus a transfusion; b. giving newborn a transfusion; c. giving mother a shot of Rhogam; *d. giving newborn a shot of Rhogam. (p. 121)

35. Most spontaneous abortions apparently occur because: *a. the fetus is defective; b. of physical traumas to the mother; c. of psychological traumas to the mother; d. the woman really didn't want the baby; e. b & c are both common causes. (p. 121)

True/False

1. A typical ejaculate has a volume of about 5 tablespoons (F, p. 92).

2. After deposit in the vagina, sperm are capable of swimming about an inch per hour (T, p. 92).

3. The process of cell division begins about 12 hours after conception (F, p. 92).

4. On the day of ovulation, a woman's basal body temperature drops (T, p. 93).

5. During the embryonic period, the lower part of the baby's body develops first (F, p. 94).

6. The mother's blood mixes freely with the baby's blood via the placenta (F, p. 94).

7. The placenta secretes large quantities of estrogen and progesterone (T, p. 95).

8. Dilation is the thinning out of the cervix (F, p. 108).

9. The fetus' central nervous system doesn't begin to develop until the second trimester (F, p. 95).

10. From the second trimester on, development of the fetus consists mainly of enlargement and differentiation of structures that are already present (T, p. 96).

11. During the 7th month, the baby generally turns from its heads-up position in the uterus to having its head down (T, p. 98).

12. At present, the commonly used pregnancy test is immunologic involving mixing a drop of urine with certain chemicals on a slide (T, p. 99).

13. Positive indications of pregnancy cannot be detected until the 4th month (T, p. 101).

14. Using Nagele's rule, if the first day of the last menstrual period was 10/30/79, the expected delivery day would be 7/27/80 (T, p. 101).

15. Women's emotions are more positive during the third trimester of pregnancy than during the other stages (F, p. 104).

16. Masters and Johnson found that a woman can usually safely resume intercourse three weeks after birth (T, p. 104).

17. Excessive alcohol consumption by a pregnant woman causes stained teeth and bone deformities in the fetus (F, p. 107).

18. Synthetic hormones like progestin can cause masculinization of a female fetus (T, p. 107).

19. The psychoactive chemical in marijuana crosses the placental barrier to the fetus (T, p. 107).

20. The incision made in the skin just behind the vagina during delivery is called an episiotomy (T, p. 109).

21. Drops of silver nitrate are placed in the newborn's eyes to prevent gonorrhea or other eye infections (T, p. 110).

22. It is during the third stage of labor that the baby is born (F, pp. 109-110).

23. Once a woman has had a cesarean delivery, she must have all subsequent deliveries that way (F, p. 110).

24. Anesthetics are prohibited with the Lamaze method (F, p. 113).

25. Historically, the use of anesthesia during childbirth was disapproved of by clergymen who argued that women's pain in childbirth was prescribed in the Bible (T, p. 113).

26. About half of the newborn babies today are breastfed (F, p. 117).

27. According to Hyde, a societal fear of nudity is one of the factors producing a decline in breastfeeding (T, p. 117).

28. Sexual responsiveness returns more quickly after birth to women who breastfeed than to women who don't (T, p. 117).

29. Although breastfeeding is associated with a slightly reduced risk of pregnancy, breastfeeding is an ineffective contraceptive (T, p. 117).

30. Rupture of the fallopian tube resulting from a tubal pregnancy can cause shock and death (T, p. 118).

31. In pseudocyesis, a woman may show signs and symptoms of pregnancy without really being pregnant (T, p. 118).

32. Amniocentesis involves insertion of a tube into the uterus to draw off some of the baby's blood (F, p. 120).

33. A couple is defined as **infertile** if they have an absolute factor preventing conception (F, p. 122).

Matching

____ 1. effleurage

____ 2. effacement

____ 3. amniocentesis

____ 4. pseudocyesis

____ 5. dilation

____ 6. episiotomy

____ 7. colostrum

____ 8. lochia

a. a discharge from the uterus and vagina that occurs during the first few weeks after childbirth.

b. opening up of the cervix during childbirth.

c. condition is which a woman shows signs of pregnancy when she is not pregnant.

d. an incision made at the vaginal entrance during delivery.

e. procedure of inserting tube into the abdomen of a pregnant woman to remove some amniotic fluid for analysis.

f. thinning out of the cervic during childbirth.

g. hormone which stimulates the breasts to produce milk.

h. light circular stroking of the abdomen with the fingertips during labor.

i. thin yellow fluid which comes out of the nipples of a pregnant woman.

<u>Matching answer key:</u> 1. h; 2. f; 3. e; 4. c; 5. b; 6. d; 7. i; 8. a.

CHAPTER 6: BIRTH CONTROL

I. LEARNING OBJECTIVES

Study of this chapter should enable the student to:

1. Specify the reasons for using contraceptives and for not using them.

2. Compare and contrast each of the available contraceptive methods from the standpoint of their history, how they work, their potential short- and/or long-term side effects, effectiveness, advantages, disadvantages, and reversibility.

3. Indicate how theoretical and actual contraceptive failure rates are determined and what these rates are for each of the contraceptives.

4. Describe the principles and procedures involved in the various versions of the rhythm method.

5. Indicate the prevalence of sterilization in the United States.

6. Describe the procedures, advantages, and disadvantages for each of the methods of male and female sterilization, and indicate the extent to which each of the methods is reversible.

7. Specify the psychological processes which may increase the likelihood of unwanted pregnancy and indicate how many unwanted pregnancies occur annually.

8. Describe the procedures, advantages and disadvantages of each of the currently available abortion methods.

9. Describe the current state of research on the development of each of the new contraceptive methods.

10. Describe the contributions of Sanger to our understanding and/or acceptance of contraceptive use.

11. Define the terms amniocentesis, iatrogenesis, and nihilism as they are used in this chapter.

II. CHAPTER AT A GLANCE

Introduction (p. 126)

Reasons For, and Arguments Against Using Contraceptives (pp. 126-129)
Reasons for Using Contraceptives
Avoiding health risks to the mother: Notes the dangers of
pregnancy for some women, aggravation of diabetes.
Spacing pregnancies: Decreases infant mortality.
Avoiding having children with birth defects
Improving early marital adjustment
Limiting family size
Avoiding pregnancy among unmarried people
Permitting more self-actualization for women: Avoid career
disruption.
Avoid having unwanted children
Curbing population growth
Arguments Against Using Contraceptives
Ethical arguments: Catholic Church's position.
Loss of spontaneity
Health risks
Racist genocide

The Pill (pp. 129-136): Focuses on combination pills, as they are
most widely used.
How It Works
Effectiveness: Distinguishes between actual and theoretical
failure rates.
Side Effects: Reviews the research, suggests the conditions
under which women should not use the pill, but notes that
pill may be safer than pregnancy.
Advantages and Disadvantages
Reversibility
Other Kinds of Pills: Reviews combination, sequential, progestin-
only, mini-pill, and morning after pill.

The IUD (pp. 136-138): Gives history.
How It Works: Notes that we aren't sure.
Effectiveness
Side Effects: Reviews the research, discusses history of Dalkon
shield, and suggests which women should not use the IUD.
Advantages and Disadvantages
Reversibility

The Diaphragm (pp. 138-140): Describes it and its history.
How It Works
Effectiveness
Side Effects
Advantages and Disadvantages
Reversibility

The Condom (pp. 140-141): Describes it and its history.
    How It Works
    Effectiveness
    Side Effects
    Advantages and Disadvantages
    Reversibility

Spermicides (PP. 141-142)
    How They Work
    Effectiveness
    Side Effects
    Advantages and Disadvantages

Douching (p. 142): Notes that it's not effective.

Withdrawal (pp. 142-143)
    Effectiveness: Not very.
    Side Effects
    Advantages and Disadvantages

The Rhythm Method (pp. 143-145)
    The Calendar Method
    The Basal Body Temperature
    The Cervical Mucus (Ovulation) Method
    Other Methods: Describes litmus-type test, saliva tests, but
        says that they are still in experimental stages.
    Effectiveness
    Advantages and Disadvantages

Sterilization (pp. 145-149): Increasingly popular, especially among
    married couples over 30 years of age.
    Male Sterilization: Describes vasectomy.
        How it works
        Effectiveness
        Side effects
        Reversibility
        Advantages and disadvantages
    Female Sterilization: Describes tubal ligation, laparotomy, and
        endoscopy.
        How it works
        Effectiveness
        Side effects
        Reversibility
        Advantages and disadvantages

Psychological Aspects: Attitudes Toward Contraception (pp. 149-150)
    Presents Sandberg & Jacobs (1971) list of ten psychological fac-
    tors that cause ineffective use (or no use) of contraception in-
    cluding denial, love, guilt, shame and embarrassment, coital
    gamesmanship, gender identity conflicts, hostility, nihilism,
    opportunism, and iatrogenic reactions.

66

Abortion (pp. 150-153): Discusses Supreme Court decisions briefly.
    Abortion Procedures
        Vacuum curettage
        Dilation and curettage
        Induced labor
        Hysterotomy
        Other methods: Describes early abortion, menstrual regulation.
    Psychological Aspects: Research difficult, but abortion does not
        appear to lead to psychological disturbance.

New Advances (pp. 153-157): Discusses attempts to develop male
    pill, immunological approaches, long-lasting hormone shots, sub-
    dermal hormone implants, vaginal rings, and other variations on
    the pill and IUD.

Summary (p. 157)

Suggestions for Further Reading (pp. 157-159)

Focuses:

    Margaret Sanger: Birth Control Pioneer (pp. 130-131);
    A Woman Tells About Her Abortion Experience (pp. 154-155);
    A Brief Summary of the History of the Development of
        Sophisticated Methods of Contraception (p. 156).

III. GLOSSARY

abortion. The ending of a pregnancy and the expulsion of the con-
    tents of the uterus; may be spontaneous or induced by human
    intervention.

abstinence (sexual). Not engaging in sexual activity.

coitus interruptus. See withdrawal.

condom. A male contraceptive sheath that is placed over the penis.

contraceptive technique. A method of preventing conception.

diaphragm. A cap-shaped rubber contraceptive device that fits
    inside a woman's vagina, over the cervix.

hysterotomy. A method of abortion sometimes used during the
    second trimester.

intrauterine device (IUD). A plastic or metal device that is
    inserted into the uterus for contraceptive purposes.

laparoscopy. A method of female sterilization.

rhythm method. A method of birth control that involves abstaining from sexual intercourse during the fertile days of the woman's menstrual cycle.

spermicide. A substance that kills sperm.

sterile. Incapable of reproducing.

sterilization technique. A procedure by which an individual is made incapable of reproducing.

tubal ligation. A surgical method of female sterilization.

vasectomy. A surgical procedure for male sterilization involving severing of the vas deferens.

withdrawal. A method of birth control in which the male withdraws his penis from the vagina before he ejaculates.

IV. AUDIO-VISUAL AIDS

Movies:

Contraception. Media Guild, 23 min., color, $345/$35. Describes condoms, diaphragms, IUDs, the pill, and the rhythm method in terms of developmental history, contraceptive principles, advantages, disadvantages and effectiveness. Shows a man putting on a condom, a woman inserting a diaphragm, and a doctor inserting an IUD in a woman. Describes male and female sterilization and shows the processes involved.

A Far Cry From Yesterday. Perennial, #1022-68, 20 min., color, $275/$28. Presents a dramatized version of what happens to the early passionate relationship of a teen-aged couple who were using foam but stopped because it was too much trouble. When the girl becomes pregnant, they decide to marry. Scenes of early optimism over the pregnancy and marriage are interposed with scenes after the arrival of the baby at which point the parents engage in constant harrangues. The drama is a bit overdone, but the film is useful for introducing a discussion of teen-age marriage motivated by pregnancy.

Four Young Women. Perennial, #1044, 20 min., color, $285/$28.50. Narration and first person descriptions of why each of four women chose to have abortions. Situations include an unmarried couple who are not yet ready to marry, a woman who had just ended a relationship when she discovered she was pregnant, a couple who married because they discovered they were pregnant and have become pregnant again, and an unmarried high school student. The movie ends with a brief description of the medical aspects of abortion and a discussion of the importance of effective contraception. Students have commented that the presentations seemed overly optimistic, however the movie is well done.

Young, Single, and Pregnant. Perennial, #1043, 18 min., color, $265/$26.50. This film is similar in format to Four Young Women except that the four women who are portrayed discuss their reasons for the choices (adoption, abortion, marriage, and single parenthood) that they made when they became premaritally pregnant. Nicely done.

Early Abortion. Perennial, #1055, 8 min., color, $130/$13. This film is well narrated by Adrienne Barbeau and provides a clear description of the use of vacuum aspiration abortion through diagrams. The actual procedure is filmed, and there is a group question and answer session dealing with the after effects of abortion, post-abortion infection, effects of abortion on future pregnancy, and the length of time until menstruation resumes.

Tapes:

Population. Norton, #340120, 60 min., $14.00. Discusses the influence of population pressures on sex. Presents demonstrations of animal experiments and their implications for population. Changes in reproduction practices and laws associated with reproduction are prophesized.

V. DEMONSTRATIONS OR GROUP DISCUSSION

A. Contraception or abortion clinic speakers: Planned Parenthood, family planning clinics, and abortion clinics usually employ people for presentations of their programs to community and school groups. They generally cover a range of topics from the ways in which their clinics operate to current social and legislative issues, and in our experience, student response to these presentations has been excellent.

B. Values clarification on contraception: This exercise helps students clarify their own values about the relative advantages and disadvantages of various methods of contraception, who should take responsibility for contraception, etc. You may use the same instructions as those for the Introductory Values Clarification Exercise given in Chapter 1, but substitute the following list of characters.

CONTRACEPTIVE VALUES CLARIFICATION

Rank order the following people from 1 through 8 indicating a 1 for the person you most like or admire and a 8 for the person you least like or admire.

___BETH is a junior in college. She has a steady boyfriend. They engage in heavy necking and petting, but she refuses to have intercourse with him because she fears pregnancy. She is aware of birth control methods, but refuses to use anything but abstinence.

___ANNE is a junior in college. She has had a steady relationship with Mark for 2 years. For the last year they have been sleeping together on a regular basis and generally have intercourse 2 or 3 times a week. Anne uses no form of contraception. Although she is familiar with contraceptive methods, she believes that "it can't happen to me."

___CAROL is a junior in college. She has no regular boyfriend, but dates frequently, and often goes to a bar to meet someone for the evening. She has sex fairly frequently after meeting someone in this situation, and often has intercourse once or twice a week. She uses no form of contraception because she feels she doesn't have sex on a regular enough basis to warrant it. Also, because she doesn't have a regular boyfriend, using something like birth control pills makes her feel cheap, like she's out looking for it.

___DIANE is a junior in college. She has been going with John for a little more than a year. They have been living together since the start of school this year, and they have sex frequently. Diane takes birth control pills because a pregnancy or a forced early marriage would cause friction with her family and ruin her career plans.

___ELLEN is a junior in college. She has no regular boyfriend, but dates frequently and often goes to a bar to meet new people. She has sex fairly often, usually once or twice a week. She takes birth control pills because she is sexually active and dislikes the idea of getting pregnant and possibly being forced into marriage. Her motto is "be prepared."

___FRAN is a junior in college. She has no regular boyfriend but dates frequently and often goes to a bar to meet new people. She has sex fairly often, usually once or twice a week. She is afraid of the health risks associated with birth control pills, but still feels that some form of contraception is necessary for her. She carries a condom in her purse, and whenever she has sex with a male, she makes sure that he uses it.

___MIKE is a junior in college. He has no regular girlfriend, but dates frequently and generally has sex once or twice a week. He alqays uses a condom because he feels contraception is important and knows that college women often do not use adequate methods. He also feels that he should share in the responsibility for contraception.

___DAVID is 35 and has been married for 10 years. He and his wife have two children, ages 7 and 4. After their second child, they decided they shouldn't have any more. So three years ago, David had a vasectomy. He feels that it helps avoid the health risks associated with his wife using contraceptives, and thinks it also represents his fair responsibility for contraception.

VI. EVALUATION MATERIALS

Essay or research questions

1. Describe each of the arguments against the use of contraceptives and evaluate them in the context of the reasons for using contraceptives. (See pp. 126-128 for arguments for contraceptives and p. 129 for arguments against contraceptives.)

2. Describe how the pill works including a discussion of the hormones involved and the possible side effects. (See pp. 129-136; students may read the results of latest research on side effects of oral contraceptives for a research paper.)

3. Name and describe the methods that may be used to increase the effectiveness of the use of rhythm for birth control. (See pp. 143-145.)

4. What are the advantages and disadvantages of vasectomies as a method of birth control. (See p. 148; students might do a paper on the latest data regarding the development of reversible vasectomies.)

5. Name, compare, and contrast the various methods of abortion in terms of the procedures involved, the amount of time, the expense, and the length of time after conception it is typically performed. (See pp. 150-153; students may want to examine local agencies to determine what methods they are using.)

Multiple choice

1. Contraceptive use was illegal in Connecticut as recently as:
   a. 1975; *b. 1965; c. 1945; d. 1930. (p. 126)

2. When births are only one year apart, the death rate for babies
   is about ___ higher than when births are two years apart.
   a. 5%; b. 25%; *c. 50%; d. 75%. (p. 127)

3. The reasoning behind the Catholic Church's argument against
   contraception is that it: a. violates "natural law"; b. involves destruction of life; c. involves destruction of the potential for life; *d. all of the above. (p. 129)

4. The ___ pill is the most widely used. *a. combination; b. sequential; c. intermediate; d. progestin-only. (p. 129)

5. The pill: a. prevents ovulation; b. keeps cervical mucus very
   thin; c. changes the lining of the uterus to make implantation
   unlikely; *d. both a & c; e. all of the above. (p. 129)

6. The combination pill has a theoretical failure rate of ___ and
   an actual failure rate of ___. *a. 0.5%, 2-5%; b. 5%, 8-10%;
   c. 10%, 10%; d. 10%, 15%; e. 0%, 0%. (p. 132)

7. Present evidence indicates that the most serious side effect of
   the pill is: a. cancer; *b. blood clotting problems; c. chlo-
   asma; d. nausea; e. creating permanent sterility. (p. 132)

8. Research on the relationship between pill use and sexual desire
   has shown that some women report ___ in desire. a. an increase;
   b. a decrease; c. neither a nor b as there has been no research
   on the relationship between desire and pill use; *d. both a & b.
   (pp. 133-134)

9. Which of the following does not belong with the others? a. laparoscopy; *b. condoms; c. vasectomy; d. tubal ligation.
   (pp. 145-149)

10. ___ has the most estrogen. a. The combination pill; b. The
    sequential pill; c. The progestin-only pill; *d. The morning
    after pill. (p. 136)

11. The death rates for the pill vs. pregnancy and childbirth are
    ___ and ___ per 100,000. a. 17, 3; b. 12, 9; *c. 3, 17; d. 9,
    12. (p. 134)

12. The major side effect of the ___ pill is that it may produce
    very irregular menstrual cycles. a. combination; b. sequential;
    *c. progestin-only; d. morning after. (p. 136)

13. According to the most accepted current hypothesis, the IUD's
    effectiveness comes from: a. changing levels of hormones;
    b. changed functioning of the fallopian tubes; *c. preventing
    implantation of the egg; d. preventing ovulation; e. all of the
    above. (p. 137)

14. The IUD is the ___ effective nonpermanent contraceptive method.
a. most; *b. second most; c. third most; d. fourth most.
(p. 137)

15. Serious side effect(s) of the IUD include: a. perforation of
the uterus; b. uterine infection; c. tubal infection; d. both
a & b; *e. all of the above. (pp. 137-138)

16. Over 5 year's time, the cheapest method of contraception is:
a. sterilization; b. pill; c. condom; *d. IUD. (p. 138)

17. The theoretical failure rate of the condom is about: a. 0.5%;
b. 1%; *c. 3%; d. 15%; e. 40%. (p. 141)

18. The ___ rhythm method has the major drawback of determining
safe days only after ovulation. a. calendar; *b. basal body
temperature; c. cervical mucus; d. all of the above. (p. 143)

19. Vasectomies: a. interfere with hormone production; b. interfere
with the sensation of ejaculation; *c. have an initial failure
rate of 0.15%; d. markedly reduce the amount of fluid the man
ejaculates. (p. 146)

20. The most common form of female sterilization is: a. hysterectomy; *b. tubal ligation; c. cophorectomy; d. endoscopy.
(p. 148)

21. Which of the following group of women is in the highest-risk
group if they use the pill? a. women who have never had children; *b. women over 40 who smoke; c. women who have severe
menstrual cramps and are 10-20 lbs. overweight; d. women who
have been on the pill for more than 5 years. (p. 134)

22. The Supreme Court decriminalized abortion in ___ by denying the
states' rights to regulate early abortion. a. 1953; b. 1967;
c. 1970; *d. 1973; e. 1977. (pp. 150-151)

23. Although the ___ used to be the most common abortion technique,
it has been replaced by the ___ as it does not involve hospi-
talization, general anesthesia, or as many risks of complications. a. vacuum curettage (D & E), dilation & curettage (D &
C); b. induced labor, dilation & curettage (D & C); *c. dilation & curettage (D & C), vacuum curettage (D & E); d. prostaglandin, induced labor. (pp. 151-152)

24. Saline induced abortion, compared with the prostaglandin method:
a. induces labor more quickly; b. produces shorter labor; *c. has
less chance of excessive bleeding and retained placenta; d. all
of the above. (p. 152)

25. The predominant mood of women after abortion is: a. guilt and shame; b. psychological disturbance; *c. relief and happiness; d. depression. (p. 153)

26. The lowest death rate (1.7 per 100,000) comes from: a. normal childbirth; *b. suction abortions; c. induced labor abortions; d. hysterotomy abortions. (p. 153)

27. ___, involving an injection of progesterone every 3 months, has the effectiveness of combination pills and is being used on a limited basis to check for side effects. a. male contraception; b. male immunology; *c. depo-provera; d. subdermal implants of a progestin capsule. (p. 157)

28. Which of these aspects of the progress toward modern contraception occurred first? a. Supreme Court denial of states' rights regarding abortion; b. Graffenberg's publication of research on the intra-uterine silver and copper ring; c. Knaus & Oginos' description of "safe and unsafe" periods of women's menstrual cycles; *d. first vasectomy operation; e. the isolation of progesterone by Corner & Beard. (p. 156)

True/False

1. There is evidence that use of contraception helps to enhance sexual satisfaction in early marriage (T, p. 127).

2. The majority of Catholics do not use contraceptives other than abstinence and rhythm (F, p. 129).

3. Every method of contraception is safer for a woman that is a pregnancy carried to term (T, p. 129).

4. The progestin in birth control pills inhibits the development of the endometrium (T, p. 132).

5. If a woman forgets to take a pill one day, but takes 2 the next day, there appears to be no appreciable increase in pregnancy risk (T, p. 132).

6. Women on the pill have a decreased susceptibility to gonorrhea (F, p. 133).

7. During a year of unprotected intercourse, women who have never taken the pill are much more likely to get pregnant than women who have just gone off the pill (F, p. 135).

8. Expulsion of the IUD is most likely in women who have had children as their cervical opening is larger (F, p. 137).

9. There is no evidence that the IUD causes cancer (T, p. 138).

10. A disadvantage of the IUD is that it interferes with the use of tampons during menstruation (F, p. 138).

11. Most failures of the diaphragm are due to improper use rather than to the device itself (T, p. 139).

12. A woman should wait at least 3 months after removal of the IUD before attempting to conceive (F, p. 138).

13. The diaphragm and contraceptive foams should both be left in the vagina for 6-8 hours after intercourse (T, pp. 138-139).

14. The actual failure rate for spermicides without additional birth control methods is about 25% (T, p. 141).

15. Douching with coke will prevent pregnancy (F, p. 142).

16. Sterilization is the most common form of birth control for married couples over 30 (T, p. 146).

17. Each year in the U.S., 1-2 million unwanted pregnancies occur (T, p. 149).

18. If 100 women have intercourse for 1 year using no contraceptives, about 80 of them will be pregnant by the end of the year (T, p. 158).

19. Women whose request for abortion is denied have much higher rates of psychological disturbance than women whose request for abortion is granted (T, p. 153).

20. A male contraceptive has been developed and is now being tested which inhibits sperm production without affecting sex drive (F, p. 154).

Matching

___ 1. birth control pill

___ 2. IUD

___ 3. diaphragm & jelly

___ 4. condom

___ 5. vaginal foam

a. requires no memory or motivation.

b. 15-20% actual failure rate, also provides protection against VD.

c. lowest actual failure rate of the 5 methods.

d. no side effects; has actual failure rate of 20-25%.

e. highest actual failure rate of these 5 methods.

Matching answer key: 1. c; 2. a; 3. d; 4. b; 5. e.

CHAPTER 7: THE PHYSIOLOGY OF SEXUAL RESPONSE

I. LEARNING OBJECTIVES

Study of this chapter should enable the student to:

1. Describe the history of scientific work on the physiology of sexual response.

2. Describe the two basic physiological processes that occur during the sexual response cycle, and trace the changes which occur at each stage of the cycle for males and for females.

3. Understand why definitions of female orgasm have been elusive. How would a man know if a woman was faking an orgasm?

4. Indicate how the refractory period affects human sexual response.

5. Describe the history, research, and current status of the debate on the clitoral vs. vaginal orgasm.

6. Define what multiple orgasm is and give the various estimates of its incidence in the population.

7. Describe the components of spinal cord reflexes and indicate how they work using erection and ejaculation as examples.

8. Specify the reasons that mechanisms of arousal are assumed to be similar in men and in women.

9. Describe the role of the brain and limbic system in sexual response, and indicate what is meant by the pleasure center.

10. Differentiate activating from organizing effects on hormones.

11. Know the relative influence of hormones and the brain in the sexuality of lower vs. higher species, and describe the influence of testosterone on male and female sexuality.

12. Define "pheromones" and know the evidence which exists for their effects on animal and human behavior.

13. Define vasocongestion, myotonia, carpopedal spasms, refractory period, limbic system, Whitten effect, Bruce effect, exaltolide, retrograde ejaculation, and Kluver-Bucy syndrome.

14. Specify how Freud, Olds, and Masters & Johnson have contributed to our knowledge in this area.

II. CHAPTER AT A GLANCE

<u>Introduction</u>: Notes that Masters & Johnson's work provides most
of the foundation for this chapter (p. 162).

<u>The Four Stages of Sexual Response</u> (pp. 162-171): Defines vasocon-
gestion and myotonia and describes the physical changes associated with each of the stages below.
<u>Excitement</u>
<u>Plateau</u>
<u>Orgasm</u>: Includes distinction between male and female orgasm.
<u>Resolution</u>: Includes discussion of refractory periods.

<u>Other Findings of the Masters and Johnson Research</u> (pp. 171-173)
<u>Clitoral Orgasm Versus Vaginal Orgasm</u>
<u>Multiple Orgasm in Women</u>

<u>Hormonal and Neural Control of Sexual Behavior</u> (pp. 173-179)
<u>The Brain, the Spinal Cord, and Sex</u>
<u>Spinal reflexes</u>: Defines receptors, transmitters, and
effectors.
<u>Mechanisms of erection</u>
<u>Mechanism of ejaculation</u>
<u>Mechanisms in women</u>
<u>Brain control</u>: Discusses limbic system, the Kluver-Bucy
syndrome, etc.
<u>Hormones and Sex</u>
<u>Organizing vs. activating effects</u>
<u>Testosterone and libido</u>

<u>Pheromones</u> (pp. 179-180)

<u>Summary</u> (p. 181)

<u>Suggestions for Further Reading</u> (p. 181)

<u>Focus</u>:

<u>William Masters and Virginia Johnson</u> (pp. 166-168)

III. GLOSSARY

<u>carpopedal spasm</u>. A spastic contraction of the hands or feet
which may occur during orgasm.

<u>climax</u>. An orgasm.

<u>coitus</u>. Sexual intercourse; insertion of the penis into the
vagina.

detumescence. The return of an erect penis to the flaccid (unaroused) state.

ejaculation. The expulsion of semen from the penis, usually during orgasm.

myotonia. Muscle tension.

orgasm. An intense sensation that occurs at the peak of sexual
arousal and is followed by release of sexual tensions.

orgasmic platform. The thickening of the walls of the outer
third of the vagina that occurs during sexual arousal.

pheromones. Chemical substances secreted outside the body that
are important in communication between animals.

plateau phase. Masters and Johnson's term for the second phase
of sexual response, occurring just before orgasm.

refractory period. The period following orgasm during which the
male cannot be sexually aroused.

resolution phase. Masters and Johnson's term for the last phase
of sexual response, in which the body returns to the unaroused
state.

sex flush. A rashlike condition on the skin that occurs during
sexual arousal.

vasocongestion. An accumulation of blood in the blood vessels
of a region of the body, especially the genitals; a swelling
or erection results.

IV. AUDIO-VISUAL AIDS

Movies:

The Sexually Mature Adult. Media Guild, 16 min., color, $240/
$25. This is an excellent film which portrays four different
couples and the variations in their experiences as they proceed through the sexual response cycle. Live sequences,
verbal subjective descriptions, and diagrams are well-integra-
ted to present the physiological and emotional aspects of
sexual intercourse.

Physiological responses of the sexually stimulated female in the
laboratory. Focus Internat'l, 16 min., color, 1975, $290/$50.
Shows sex flush, pupil changes and other external responses,
plus EKG and X-ray films of vaginal changes as women masturbate to orgasm.

Physiological responses of the sexually stimulated male in the
laboratory. Focus Internat'l, 16 min., color, 1975, $290/$50.
Shows erection, ejaculation, scrotal changes, skin flush and
sweating, heart, respiratory, and motor changes, and effects
of caressing and temperature.

Tapes:

Sexual processes. Norton, #34004X, 60 min., $14.00. Discusses
distinction between the phases of sexual response. Personal
interpretations of the meaning of orgasm to the individual
are presented. The effects of drugs, aphrodisiacs and various
orgastic mechanisms are discussed.

V. DEMONSTRATIONS OR GROUP DISCUSSION

Beliefs about physiological responses: During the class session
before you begin this chapter, ask students to write down several
questions, anonymously, regarding their own sexual responses. Collect these questions, redistribute them to class members, and ask
them to write answers to these questions. Finally, collect the
questions and answers, arrange them by topic, and begin the next
class session by reading some of them. This generally provides
some humor and gives you an opportunity to correct some common but
erroneous beliefs.

VI. EVALUATION MATERIALS

Essay or research questions

1. Compare and contrast male and female physiological responses during each of the four stages of sexual response. (See pp. 162-171.)

2. Compare and contrast the reasoning behind Freud's versus Masters
and Johnson's conclusions on the clitoral versus vaginal orgasm
debate. (See pp. 171-172.)

3. How did the discovery of the Kluver-Bucy syndrome add to our
knowledge of the brain's role in sexual behavior? (See p. 176.)

4. Give an example of the organizing (or activating) effect of a
hormone. (See pp. 177-178.)

5. What animal and human evidence exists to support the notion that
there are "pleasure centers" in the brain? (See p. 177; students
may want to use this question for a research paper.)

6. Review the latest research on the influence of pheromones on
animal and human sexual attraction. (See pp. 179-180.)

Multiple choice

1. Most of our scientific knowledge of the physiology of sexual response is due to the work of: a. Krafft-Ebing; b. Ellis; c. Kinsey; d. Montalnbalm; *e. Masters & Johnson. (p. 162)

2. The basic physiological processes during the excitement phase are: *a. vasocongestion and myotonia; b. orgasm and resolution; c. tension and arousal; d. erotic thoughts. (pp. 163-164)

3. Erection may be produced by: a. direct physical stimulation of the genitals; b. stimulation of nongenital parts of the body; c. erotic thoughts; *d. all of the above. (p. 163)

4. Vaginal lubrication is caused by secretions from the: a. Bartholin's glands; b. Cowper's glands; *c. vaginal walls; d. uterus. (p. 164)

5. During the sexual response cycle, erection in the male corresponds most closely to ___ in the female. a. the tenting effect; *b. vaginal lubrication; c. formation of orgasmic platform; d. secretion of Bartholin's glands; e. contraction of uterus. (p. 164)

6. Nipple erection is due largely to ___ and breast swelling is due to ___. *a. myotonia, vasocongestion; b. vasocongestion, myotonia; c. myotonia, myotonia; d. vasocongestion, vasocongestion. (p. 164)

7. During the excitement phase, the ___ of the vagina expands dramatically. a. lower (outer) third; b. lower two-thirds; *c. upper two-thirds; d. upper third. (p. 164)

8. During the excitement phase, there is: a. an increase in blood pressure; b. an increase in pulse rate; *c. both a & b; d. a decrease in blood pressure. (p. 164)

9. Scrotal skin ___ during arousal. *a. gets thicker; b. gets thinner; c. allows the testes to move further from the body; d. becomes pale in color. (p. 164)

10. Vasocongestion reaches its peak during the ___ phase. a. excitement; *b. plateau; c. orgasm; d. resolution. (p. 164)

11. During arousal, the size of the testes: a. decreases by as much as 50%; b. does not change; *c. increases by as much as 50%; d. has not been measured. (p. 165)

12. During the plateau phase, the clitoris: a. becomes 50% longer; *b. becomes 50% shorter; c. does not change in length; d. none of the above. (p. 165)

13. Carpopedal spasms are: *a. contractions of the muscles of the feet and hands during orgasm; b. caused by chronic pelvic congestion; c. arhythmic spasms of the heart recorded during particularly intense orgasm; d. none of the above. (p. 169)

14. The distinction between clitoral and vaginal orgasm was originated by: a. Kinsey; b. Hite; *c. Freud; d. Masters & Johnson. (p. 171)

15. Masters and Johnxon's conclusion that a distinction between clitoral and vaginal orgasms is senseless is based on their finding that: a. all female orgasms are physiologically the same, regardless of the locus of stimulation; b. clitoral stimulation is almost always involved in producing orgasm; *c. both a & b; d. none of the above. (p. 172)

16. According to Hyde, female orgasmic capacity seems to be limited; a. to 20 orgasms; b. to 50 orgasms; c. by her responsiveness; *d. by her lover's endurance. (p. 173)

17. The ejaculation reflex works much the same as the erection reflex except that: *a. the ejaculation center is located higher in the spinal cord; b. the parasympathetic nervous system is involved; c. the response involves blood vessels; d. all of the above. (p. 174)

18. Male and female reflex mechanisms of arousal are assumed to be similar because: a. vasocongestion and myotonia operate similarly in both genders; b. their genital organs are derived from the same embryonic tissue; c. female lubrication and male erection responses are physiologically similar; *d. all of the above. (p. 176)

19. Destruction of the temporal lobes of the brain (Kluver-Bucy syndrome) produces: a. a loss of arousability; b. a loss of sexual interest; c. both a & b; *d. hypersexuality and increased eroticism. (p. 176)

20. Rats will do without ___ in order to press a lever to stimulate their "pleasure centers" repeatedly. a. food, but not sleep; b. food and sleep, but won't endure pain; *c. food and sleep, and they will endure pain; d. none of the above. (p. 177)

21. The ___ effect of hormones is illustrated by the finding that an adult male rat who is castrated and then given testosterone will start engaging in sex again. *a. activating; b. initiating; c. organizing; d. restorative. (p. 178)

22. Pheromones are: a. biochemicals; b. secreted into the bloodstream; c. secreted outside the body; d. both a & b; *e. both a & c. (p. 179)

23. Exaltolide (synthetic compound with a musklike odor which may be similar to pheromones) can be perceived by: a. adult males; b. prepubescent males; *c. adult females; d. prepubescent females; e. both a & b. (p. 180)

24. Prior to his work on the physiology of sexual response, Masters did extensive work on: *a. postmenopausal hormone replacement therapy; b. primate sexual response; c. identification of human pheromones; d. all of the above. (p. 168)

True/False

1. Myotonia refers to a great deal of blood flowing into the blood vessels as a result of their dilation (F, p. 162).

2. Penile erection and vaginal lubrication result from the same physiological process (T, p. 164).

3. The appearance of lubrication is a good indicator that a woman is close to orgasm (F, p. 164).

4. Many males have nipple erection during the excitement phase (T, p. 164).

5. The orgasmic platform is the swelling of the tissues surrounding the outer third of the vagina (T, p. 165).

6. The size of the vaginal entrance becomes smaller during the plateau phase (T, p. 165).

7. Orgasm and ejaculation in the male are different names for the same process (F, p. 168).

8. Orgasm contractions occur at about 0.8 second intervals in the male and at about 1.6 second intervals in the female (F, pp. 168-169).

9. During female orgasm, the uterus contracts rhythmically in waves from the top of the uterus down toward the cervix (T, p. 169).

10. Orgasmic sensations appear to be more intense for males than for females (F, p. 169).

11. Orgasm is the final phase in the sexual response cycle (F, p. 170).

12. During resolution, the nipples may appear to become erect (T, p. 170).

13. The refractory period refers to the length of time during which stimulation cannot produce arousal (T, p. 171).

14. Women have a longer refractory period than men (F, p. 171).

15. There is more variability in male than in female orgasm patterns (F, p. 173).

16. Several important components of sexual behavior, including erection and ejaculation, are controlled by fairly simple spinal cord reflexes (T, p. 173).

17. Physical stimulation of the male genitals produces a neural signal which is transmitted to an erection center in the lowest part of the spinal cord (T, p. 174).

18. Physical stimulation of the genitals will not produce erections in men with severed spinal cords (F, p. 174).

19. Ejaculation can often be controlled voluntarily (T, p. 175).

20. Retrograde ejaculation is quite harmful and should be treated as soon as possible (F, p. 176).

21. Ejaculation involves both internal and external sphincter muscles (T, p. 175).

22. In experiments with monkeys, it was found that stimulation of the limbic system produces arousal, but no such research has been done with humans (F, p. 176).

23. Sexual behavior of lower species is more hormonally controlled than is that of higher species (T, p. 178).

24. If all sources of androgen are removed from women, they cannot be aroused (T, p. 179).

25. If a mouse that has just conceived is exposed to the odors of a strange male mouse, the pregnancy is aborted (T, p. 179).

26. Chemicals known to be sex-attractant pheromones in monkeys have not yet been found in humans (F, p. 180).

CHAPTER 8: TECHNIQUES OF AROUSAL

I. LEARNING OBJECTIVES

Study of this chapter should enable the student to:

1. Describe the ways in which our sexual expression may be helped or hindered by the increased number of sex manuals.

2. Know what is meant by "erogenous zones."

3. Compare male and female methods of masturbation.

4. Compare the incidence and themes of fantasy during masturbation by males and females.

5. Indicate the role and effects of fantasy during marital intercourse.

6. Describe the tactile stimulation techniques used during sexual intercourse.

7. Indicate how the various non-tactile senses contribute to sexual arousal.

8. Describe the four basic coital positions, their advantages and disadvantages, and some of their variations.

9. Describe each of the following and indicate the incidence of each in our society today: cunnilingus, fellatio, sixty-nining, and anal intercourse.

10. Define the terms "aphrodisiac" and "anaphrodisiac" and describe the evidence for and against the claims that various foods and drugs function as either.

11. Knowing what is meant by "treating intercourse and orgasm as goals" and indicate Hyde's suggested alternatives.

12. Describe the problems and possible solutions that are associated with sexual inexperience and with sexual boredom.

II. CHAPTER AT A GLANCE

Introduction (p. 184)

Erogenous Zones (pp. 184-185): Defined.

One-Person Sex (pp. 185-189)
    Masturbation: Defined.
        Techniques of female masturbation: Describes them, notes that
            female behavior differs from male fantasies about female
            behavior.
        Techniques of male masturbation: Describes them, notes that
            males use less variation than females.
    Fantasy
        Fantasy during masturbation: Describes sex differences, con-
            tent, and themes.
        Fantasy during intercourse
    Vibrators, Dildos and Such: Includes discussion of body oils.

Two-Person Sex (pp. 189-199): Notes that this section avoids assump-
    tion that one of the persons is male, the other female.
    Kissing
    Touching
        Hand stimulation of the male genitals
        Hand stimulation of the female genitals
    The Other Senses
        Sights
        Smells
        Sounds
    Genital-Genital Stimulation: Positions of Intercourse
        Man-on-top
        Woman-on-top
        Rear-entry
        Side-to-side
        Other variations
    Mouth-Genital Stimulation
        Cunnilingus
        Fellatio
        Sixty-nining
    Anal Intercourse

Aphrodisiacs (pp. 199-200)
    Is There a Good Aphrodisiac? Notes that there is no known aphro-
        disiac substance.
    Anaphrodisiacs

Are Intercourse and Orgasm the Goal? (pp. 200-201): Discusses the
    problem of goal orientation and mentions the works of Rollo May
    and Marc Feigen Fasteau.

From Inexperience to Boredom (pp. 201-204)
  Sexual Inexperience: Stresses importance of communication.
  Boredom

Summary (p. 204)

Suggestions for Further Reading (p. 204)

Focus

  The Protestant ethic: Sex as work (pp. 202-203)

III. GLOSSARY

anal intercourse. Sexual behavior in which one person's penis
   is inserted into another's anus.

anaphrodisiac. A substance that decreases sexual desire.

anilingus. Mouth-anus stimulation.

aphrodisiac. A substance that increases sexual desire.

autoeroticism. Sexual self-stimulation; masturbation is one
   example.

cunnilingus. Mouth stimulation of the female genitals.

dildo. An artificial penis.

erogenous zones. Areas of the body that are particularly sensitive to sexual stimulation.

fellatio. Mouth stimulation of the penis.

intercourse (sexual). Sexual activity in which the penis is
   inserted into the vagina; coitus.

masturbation. Self-stimulation of the genitals to produce sexual arousal.

oral-genital sex. Sexual activity in which the mouth is used to
   stimulate the genitals.

IV. AUDIO-VISUAL AIDS

Movies:

Heterosexual Intercourse. Williams & Wilkins, 15 min., color.
   An attractive young couple engage in a variety of lovemaking
   techniques, including sixty-nining and intercourse. Paul R.

87

Miller, M.D., narrates and describes some of Masters & Johnson's findings. In addition to providing some desensitization, one of the best features of the film is that the man has an orgasm before the woman does, but he shows how to manually stimulate her to orgasm. Dr. Miller's definition of premature ejaculation may provide a basis for class discussion as it needs clarification.

Orange. Multi Media #365, 2 min., 40 sec., color, 1970, $55/$12. This is a beautifully filmed and erotic presentation of an orange being opened. Provides a good basis for discussing sensuality and arousal.

Free. Multi Media #155, 12 min., 1971, $200/$35. Depicts love making by a young black couple in a country setting.

Coital Positioning. Center for Marital & Sexual Studies, 12 min., color, $90/$35. Shows a couple having intercourse in a variety of coital positions including the scissors, spoon, Persian, male superior, rear entry, and female superior. May be useful for suggesting variations to couples with a limited sexual repertoire.

Fun. Center for Marital & Sexual Studies, 55 min., B&W, $395/$75. A young couple have intercourse on a waterbed and demonstrate that good sex need not be deadly serious business.

Oral Pleasuring. Center for Marital & Sexual Studies, 16 min., color, $245/$40. Deals with the controversy regarding oral sex.

Foreplay. Center for Marital & Sexual Studies, 21 min., color, $295/$50. A married couple enjoys 15 min. of foreplay in preparation for intercourse. They use a variety of physical positions, creams, lotions, etc.

V. DEMONSTRATIONS OR GROUP DISCUSSION

A. Sex Advice Columns: Have each student cut out and bring to class a column from a magazine such as Playboy or Viva that gives advice on sexual techniques. Divide the class into groups of 6-8 and have them discuss each of the columns in terms of the following questions:
1. From your own experience, is this good advice?
2. Does the author of the column seem to have any biases in favor of or against certain techniques?
3. Is it a good idea or not for people to read columns such as these?
4. Does the column encourage a "work ethic" about sex, as discussed in the Focus in Chapter 8 of the text?

5. How would you improve on the advice given in this column?

VI. EVALUATION MATERIALS

Essay or research questions

1. What is an aphrodisiac and what foods and drugs fit that definition? (See pp. 199-200.) Have there been any recent developments
in the search for aphrodisiacs?

2. How has the Protestant ethic influenced our sexual ethics? (See
pp. 200-203.) List at least 3 sexual words or phrases that reflect
our Protestant-work-ethic attitude toward sex and explain why each
is an example (key - "achieve" orgasm, "make it," "reach" orgasm,
"work out," etc.).

3. What kinds of solutions are there to the problem of sexual
boredom? (See pp. 203-204.) Review the literature on the relationship between sexual behavior and successful marriage.

Multiple choice

1. Erogenous zones: a. is a concept originated by Kinsey; b. are
   limited to the genitals, nipples, lips and ear lobes; *c. can
   vary in their location from one person to another; d. include
   only those areas containing erectile tissue. (pp. 184-185)

2. The most common female masturbation technique is: *a. manipulation of the clitoris and labia; b. insertion of a finger into the
   vagina; c. insertion of phallic objects into the vagina;
   d. genital massage by streams of water from a shower. (p. 186)

3. Typically, when males masturbate, orgasm occurs within: a. a
   few seconds; *b. a minute or two; c. 4-5 minutes; d. 10-15
   minutes. (p. 186)

4. Although male masturbation typically involves an up and down
   manual stimulation of the penis, there is variation among males
   in the: a. tightness of the grip; b. speed of movement; c. amount
   of glans stimulation; *d. all of the above. (p. 186)

5. The most common masturbation fantasy for both men and women is:
   a. being forced to have sex; b. having sex with someone of the
   same gender; *c. having sex with a stranger; d. having sex with
   more than one person at the same time. (p. 187)

6. In a long term monogamous relationship, fantasies during intercourse are: a. a sign of disloyalty to your partner; *b. a way
   to inject variety and excitement into the relationship without
   being unfaithful; c. a sign of dissatisfaction with your partner; d. an indication of impending impotence or frigidity.
   (p. 188)

7. Masters & Johnson and other sex therapists using their approach
   recommend the use of ___ in their treatment. a. dildos;
   b. long-term psychotherapy; c. artificial vaginas; *d. body
   oils. (p. 189)

8. During oral sex, vaginal deodorants are: a. a necessity so as
   not to offend; b. preferable to bathing; *c. apt to irritate
   the vagina; d. none of the above. (p. 191)

9. The most frequently used coital position in the U.S. is:
   *a. man-on-top; b. woman-on-top; c. rear-entry; d. side-to-side.
   (p. 193)

10. Man-on-top coitus is not best: a. for conception; b. for leav-
    ing the woman's hands free for body stimulation; *c. if the
    woman is in later stages of pregnancy; d. all of the above.
    (p. 194)

11. Woman-on-top coitus: a. provides a lot of clitoral stimulation;
    b. helps the man to delay his orgasm; c. is good if the man is
    tired; *d. all of the above. (p. 195)

12. "Greek style" refers to: a. rear-entry coitus; b. cunnilingus;
    c. fellatio; *d. anal intercourse. (p. 199)

13. ___ should be avoided as a lubricant for anal sex. a. saliva;
    b. K-Y jelly; *c. Vaseline; d. sterile jelly; e. all of the
    above. (p. 199)

14. ___ is an aphrodisiac. a. an oyster; b. Cantharides (Spanish
    fly); c. Amyl nitrate (poppers); d. both b & c; *e. none of the
    above. (p. 200)

15. The claim that marijuana has aphrodisiac qualities: a. has not
    received scientific documentation; b. has been made by users;
    c. may be due to its effect of stretching out time, thus pro-
    longing and intensifying sexual sensations; *d. all of the
    above. (p. 200)

16. This substance, though reputed to increase sexual feeling, is
    actually physically dangerous. a. Cantharides (Spanish fly);
    b. Amyl nitrate (poppers); *c. both of the above; d. neither
    of the above. (p. 200)

17. To deal with sexual inexperience, you should: a. question the assumption that you should be experienced; b. read some good sex manuals; c. communicate with your partner; *d. all of the above. (p. 202)

18. ___ has written about problems in applying the Protestant ethic to sexuality. a. Kinsey; *b. Slater; c. Masters and Johnson; d. Johnston; e. all of the above. (pp. 202-203)

True/False

1. Masturbation and fantasy are both examples of autoeroticism (T, p. 185).

2. Almost all men and the majority of women have masturbated (T, p. 186).

3. Almost all men but only a minority of women have masturbated (F, p. 186).

4. There is more variation in masturbation techniques among men than among women (F, p. 186).

5. Fantasies during masturbation are somewhat more frequent among men than women (T, p. 187).

6. Fantasy during intercourse is uncommon among married women (F, p. 188).

7. Women who fantasize during intercourse with their husbands have better sexual relations with their husbands than women who don't fantasize (T, p. 188).

8. We have more detailed information about the content of male than of female fantasies during intercourse (F, p. 188).

9. The best position for conception of a baby is rear-entry (F, p. 194).

10. If a man wants to control his ejaculation, man-on-top is the best coital position (F, p. 195).

11. A good position for the woman in later stages of pregnancy is side-to-side (T, p. 196).

12. The vagina has fewer bacteria than the mouth according to some health experts (T, p. 197).

13. Some women report orgasm during anal intercourse (T, p. 199).

14. The penis may safely be inserted into the vagina after anal intercourse (F, p. 199).

15. Potassium nitrate (saltpeter) decreases sex drive and makes you want to urinate frequently (F, p. 200).

CHAPTER 9: SEX RESEARCH

I. LEARNING OBJECTIVES

Study of this chapter should enable the student to:

1. Understand some of the methodological problems of sex research regarding such issues as sampling and reliability of self-reports.

2. Contrast the advantages and disadvantages of the use of interviews with use of questionnaires in collecting data on sexuality.

3. Contrast the advantages and disadvantages of self-reports versus direct observations in studying sexual behavior.

4. Know the basic ethical principles to be used by researchers, as adopted by most scientific organizations.

5. Describe the cost-benefit approach in deciding whether to conduct research.

6. Evaluate the major research projects described in this chapter with respect to how respondents were selected, how the data were collected, reliability of the data, and the extent to which the results of each of the projects can be generalized to the population as a whole.

7. Describe the major findings in each of the studies described in this chapter.

8. Indicate how correlational studies differ from experimental studies in terms of both methodology and the inferences that may be drawn from the results.

9. Discuss the ethical problems associated with each of the major studies.

10. Define the terms average, variability, normal, incidence, and frequency.

11. Design a study to try to answer a question you have about sexual behavior using each of the methods described in the chapter.

12. Indicate the contributions to our understanding of this area that have been made by Kinsey, Hunt, the Redbook and Psychology Today surveys, Westoff, Kantner & Zelnick, Sorenson, Weinberg & Williams, and Masters & Johnson.

II. CHAPTER AT A GLANCE

<u>Introduction</u> (p. 206): Gives a typology of techniques used in sex
  research.

<u>Issues in Sex Research</u> (pp. 206-210)
  <u>Sampling</u>
  <u>Reliability of Self-Reports of Sexual Behavior</u>
    <u>Purposeful distortion</u>
    <u>Memory</u>
    <u>Ability to estimate</u>
    <u>Interviews vs. questionnaires</u>
  <u>Self Reports Versus Direct Observations</u>
  <u>Extraneous Factors</u>: Discusses influence of interviewer age, gen-
    der, form of questioning, etc., on reliability of reports.
  <u>Ethical Issues</u>
    <u>Informed consent</u>
    <u>Protection from harm</u>
    <u>A cost-benefit approach</u>

<u>The Major Sex Surveys</u> (pp. 211-221)
  <u>The Kinsey Reports</u>
    <u>Sampling</u>
    <u>Interviewing</u>
    <u>Checking for accuracy</u>
    <u>How accurate are the Kinsey statistics?</u>
  <u>The Hunt Survey</u>
    <u>Sampling</u>
    <u>The questionnaire</u>
    <u>Comparing Kinsey and Hunt</u>
    <u>The sexual revolution</u>: Notes that premarital sex has in-
      creased, while gender and social class differences have
      decreased.
  <u>The Magazine Surveys</u>
    <u>The Redbook survey</u>
    <u>The Psychology Today survey</u>
  <u>Probability Samples</u>
    <u>The National Fertility Studies</u>: Describes the Westoff studies.
    <u>The Kantner and Zelnick survey</u>

<u>Studies of Special Populations</u> (pp. 221-222)
  <u>Sorenson</u: Adolescents</u>
    <u>Sampling</u>
    <u>The questionnaire</u>
  <u>Weinberg and Williams</u>: Male Homosexuals

<u>Laboratory Studies Using Direct Observations of Sexual Behavior</u>
  (pp. 222-225)

Masters and Johnson: The Physiology of Sexual Response
    Sampling
    Data collection techniques
    Ethics

Participant-Observer Studies (pp. 225-226)
    Humphreys: The Tearoom Trade
    Bartell: Swinging

Experimental Sex Research (pp. 226-227): Discusses differences
    between correlation and cause, and uses Schmidt, Sigusch, &
    Schafer's research as an example.

Some Statistical Concepts (pp. 227-229)
    Average
    Variability
    Average vs. Normal
    Incidence vs. Frequency

Summary (pp. 229-230)

Focus:

    Alfred C. Kinsey (pp. 212-214)

III. GLOSSARY

The statistical terms, defined on pages 227-229, are probably the
only problematic words in this chapter.

IV. AUDIO-VISUAL AIDS

Movies:

Pomeroy takes a sex history. Multi Media, 35 min., color.
    The use of the interview to obtain a sex history is demonstra-
    ted by Dr. Wardell Pomeroy of the Institute for Sex Research.

V. DEMONSTRATIONS OR GROUP DISCUSSION

Designing Sex Research: This exercise is to help students learn
some of the important principles of good research design, and to
give them experience in confronting some of the problems involved in
conducting adequate research.

Break the class into small groups of 5-6 students. Each group is
to design a piece of sex research that could be done on your own
campus. Students should take the following into consideration in
designing the research:

1. The research should answer some questions in which they are really interested.

2. The research should provide new information rather than re-peating a study that has already been done. Students should check their texts and question the instructor to attempt to find out whether their research will add to our knowledge.

3. Students should decide whether to use the survey or experimental method by comparing the relative strengths of each method for the question they are asking. If the survey method is chosen, students should indicate how they intend to obtain an adequate sample.

4. Students should review the principles outlined in the text to determine if they are planning to conduct their research in an ethical manner.

5. The research plan should be examined to determine the extent to which we may place confidence in the results regarding such issues as the accuracy of self reports and so forth.

6. Finally, what could be concluded from the study?

If some of the designs are particularly good, it might become a class project to carry out the studies.

VI. EVALUATION MATERIALS

Essay or research questions

1. Imagine that you are interested in conducting research aimed at determining what people first found sexually arousing in adolescence or earlier. Describe three potential sources of inaccuracy in their self reports, and indicate how the researcher may reduce these in-accuracies. (See pp. 207-209.)

2. Describe the advantages and disadvantages of the use of (a) inter-views vs. questionnaires, or (b) self-reports vs. direct observation in conducting sex research. (See pp. 208-209.)

3. You are the member of a university ethics committee that must make a decision regarding approval or disapproval of a study of sexual behavior. The researchers want to conduct research similar to Kantner & Zelnick's except that they plan to study 18-22 year old males and females. First, why would they study that age group? Second, indicate how you would apply the cost-benefit approach to your task. (See pp. 220-221 for a description of the Kantner & Zelnick study and p. 210 for discussion of the cost-benefit approach.

4. Describe how you would go about designing a study to answer a question you have about sexual behavior (a) using the survey method, then, (b) using the experimental method.

Multiple choice

1. Research indicates that those who volunteer to participate in sex research differ from those who refuse: a. in their political attitudes; b. in the extent to which they are sexually experienced; c. in their social class; d. in all of the above ways; *e. both a & b. (p. 207)

2. Most of our information about sexual behavior has come from: a. researchers' direct observations of peoples' sexual practices; *b. peoples' self-reports of their sexual practices; c. laboratory experiments on sexual behavior; d. evidence gathered by researchers acting as participant-observers. (p. 207)

3. Compared with the use of self report, direct observation in sex research tends to: a. lead to greater inaccuracy; b. increase problems of purposeful distortion; *c. be more expensive; d. increase the number of willing volunteers; e. all of the above. (p. 209)

4. The ethical standards of most scientific organizations require that researchers ___ their respondents. a. pay for the information from; b. obtain informed consent prior to participation from; c. insure the physical and psychological protection of; d. all of the above; *e. both b & c. (p. 210)

5. ___ were underrepresented in the Kinsey sample. a. college students; b. people living in cities; *c. people living west of the Mississippi; d. Protestants; e. all of the above. (p. 213)

6. Kinsey was probably most successful in minimizing problems of: *a. purposeful distortion; b. memory; c. ability to estimate; d. sampling; e. none of these. (p. 215)

7. To check the accuracy of self reports, Kinsey: a. conducted retakes of interviews with a long period of time (at least 18 months) intervening between interviews; b. compared responses of husbands and wives who had been interviewed independently; c. administered polygraph ("lie detector") tests to a portion of his sample; d. all of the above; *e. both a & b. (p. 215)

8. The statisticians who evaluated Kinsey's work felt that four of his findings might have been particularly subject to error. Which was **NOT** one of these findings? *a. generally low levels

97

of sexual activity; b. high incidence of homosexuality;
c. little difference between older and younger generations;
d. strong relationship between sexual activity and social class;
e. relationship between sexual activity and changes in social
class. (p. 216)

9. The Hunt survey obtained its sample from: a. registrars' lists
of students from 8 northeastern colleges; b. psychologists'
clients throughout the United States; *c. names in telephone
books from 24 cities throughout the United States; d. volunteers
who responded to newspaper ads placed in major metropolitan
areas; e. all of the above. (p. 216)

10. This researcher made a special point of collecting data in institutions like colleges and prisons. a. Heiman; b. Hunt;
*c. Kinsey; d. Humphreys; e. Weinberg. (p. 217)

11. Sampling procedures were probably best (in terms of representing the U.S. population) in the ___ study. a. Kinsey; *b. Hunt;
c. Sorenson; d. Bartell; e. Humphreys. (pp. 217-218)

12. All but one of the following changes has probably occurred in
the past 30 years. Which has NOT? a. premarital sex is more
common; *b. homosexuality is more common; c. gender differences
in sexuality have decreased; d. social class differences in
sexuality have decreased. (p. 218)

13. Due to the major problem of ___, the Redbook and Psychology
Today surveys are of limited value. *a. sampling bias;
b. reliability; c. ethical violations; d. statistical errors;
e. all of the above. (pp. 219-220)

14. The Westoff studies: *a. had a low refusal rate; b. gave an
unrealistically high estimate of the frequency of marital intercourse; c. eliminated the problems associated with self report;
d. both a & c; e. all of the above. (p. 220)

15. Kantner and Zelnick's survey investigated: a. homosexual behavior; b. child molesting; *c. contraceptive use by young unmarried women; d. marital dissatisfaction among couples married
at least 15 years. (pp. 220-221)

16. In the Weinberg and Williams study of homosexuality: a. a random sample of gays was obtained; b. only those gay females
belonging to activist organizations were sampled; *c. gay males
living in small towns and rural areas were underrepresented;
d. the gays who were sampled were all in therapy; e. both b &
d. (p. 222)

17. Direct observation of sexual behavior in the laboratory over-comes the problem of: a. purposeful distortion; b. inaccurate memory; c. inability of subjects to estimate; d. both a & b; *e. all of the above. (p. 209)

18. Masters and Johnsons' sample omitted: a. the unmarried; b. the sexually inexperienced; c. non-volunteers; *d. both b & c; e. all of the above. (p. 222)

19. Regarding their sampling procedures, Masters and Johnson: *a. took the position that the processes they were studying were normative, thus reducing concern with representative sampling; b. took pains to ensure that their sample was repre-sentative of the U.S. population; c. used a table of random numbers to select their sample; d. avoided paying subjects be-cause of concern that they might fake responses to obtain money; e. none of the above. (p. 224)

20. In their concern for ethics, Masters and Johnson: a. provided subjects with details of what would happen to them before they participated; b. gave subjects the opportunity to withdraw at any stage of the research; c. used only married couples; d. all of the above; *e. both a & b. (p. 225)

21. Which of the following researchers completely utilized the prin-ciple of informed consent? a. Humphreys; b. Hunt; *c. Masters and Johnson; d. both a & b; e. all of the above. (p. 225)

22. ___ obtained a sample through placing ads in newspapers. a. Humphreys; b. Heiman; c. Hunt; *d. Bartell; e. Sorenson, (p. 226)

23. On the basis of Kinsey's research, it is legitimate to conclude: *a. that women who masturbate to orgasm prior to marriage are more likely to have orgasm consistently in marriage than women who do not; b. premarital practice in masturbating to orgasm causes women to have more orgasms in marriage; c. women who avoid premarital sex have better sexual adjustment in marriage; d. both a & b; e. all of the above. (p. 226)

24. If we want to examine the influence of viewing erotic material on sexual behavior, it is best to: a. compare the amount of sexual activity engaged in by people 24 hours before exposure to erotica with the 24 hours after exposure; b. ask individuals to indicate how much their behavior is influenced by exposure to erotic material; *c. expose half the subjects to erotica and half to neutral material, then compare the amount of sexual activity engaged in by the two groups; d. conduct a 24 hour follow-up on patrons of a pornographic movie theatre to inter-view them about their sexual behavior. (p. 227)

25. The median is the: a. average of all the scores of all sub-
    jects; b. the most frequent response of subjects; *c. the score
    that splits the sample in half, with half of the subjects falling
    above and half below that score; d. none of the above. (p. 228)

26. Incidence means: a. average of all the scores of all subjects;
    *b. the percentage of people who have engaged in a certain
    behavior; c. the percentage of people who have engaged in a
    behavior before a certain age; d. how often people engage in a
    certain behavior. (p. 229)

27. "95% of males masturbate." This is a statement about:
    a. frequency; *b. incidence; c. what is normal; d. causality.
    (p. 229)

True/False

1. People are more apt to report their sexual feelings to a rea-
    searcher of the other gender than to one of the same gender
    (F, p. 209).

2. The best known study involving use of questionnaires and inter-
    views with a large sample was conducted by Hunt (F, p. 211).

3. Kinsey interviewed both blacks and whites (T, p. 211).

4. Although some segments of the population were overrepresented
    in Kinsey's sample, he used statistical methods to correct his
    sample so that it would agree with the U.S. census (T, p. 211).

5. Critics of Kinsey's works are more impressed with his sampling
    methods than with his interviewing techniques (F, p. 216).

6. Kinsey's associates felt that his most questionable statistic
    was the high incidence of male homosexuality (T, p. 216).

7. One of the purposes of Bartell's study was to compare sexual
    behavior in the 1970's with the data Kinsey had gathered 30
    years earlier (F, pp. 216, 226).

8. Heiman's study was serialized in Playboy magazine which is why
    her research is sometimes known as the "Playboy survey" (F,
    (p. 216).

9. Comparison of Hunt's and Kinsey's results suggests that there
    has been very little change in sexual behavior in the past 30
    years (F, p. 218).

10. More people responded to the Psychology Today survey than to the
    Redbook survey, therefore, Psychology Today's sample was better
    (F, p. 219).

11. The Kantner & Zelnick study provided data on differences in sexual behavior between blacks and whites (T, p. 220).

12. Because they sampled only those gay males who were open about their homosexuality, Weinberg & Williams may have provided a picture of homosexuals which emphasized their adjustment (T, p. 222).

13. Masters and Johnson's initial research on sexual response was conducted with prostitutes (T, p. 222).

14. The results of Masters and Johnson's research has been replicated by independent investigators (F, pp. 224-225).

15. Masters and Johnson's 5 year follow-up contacts indicated that only 15% of their subjects had developed any sexual dysfunction whereas the majority were unaffected by participation (F, p. 225).

16. Schmidt, Sigusch, and Schafer found that subjects rated erotic stories with affection as less arousing than erotic stories without affection (F, p. 227).

17. Females were more likely than males to report an increase in their coital activity following exposure to erotica in Schmidt, Sigusch, & Schafer's study (T, p. 227).

18. In statistical terms, we are collecting data on incidence when we ask people how often they masturbate (F, p. 229).

Matching

___ 1. Provided the first major study of sexual response in the laboratory.

___ 2. This study was commissioned by the Playboy Foundation.

___ 3. Used a probability sample to reduce sampling bias.

___ 4. Required written permission from parents for adolescents to participate.

___ 5. Used the technique known as 100% sampling.

a. Kinsey

b. Hunt

c. Westoff

d. Sorenson

e. Masters & Johnson

Matching answer key: 1. e; 2. b; 3. c; 4. d; 5. a.

Matching

___ 1. This study was written by a professional journalist.

___ 2. Investigated homosexuality cross-culturally.

___ 3. Data were coded with the un-written code known only by the few people directly involved in the project.

___ 4. Investigators for this re-search took the role of "baby swingers."

___ 5. Sampled only young women between 15 and 19 years of age.

a. Kinsey

b. Hunt

c. Kantner & Zelnick

d. Weinberg & Williams

e. Bartell

Matching answer key: 1. b; 2. d; 3. a; 4. e; 5. c.

CHAPTER 10: SEXUALITY AND THE LIFE CYCLE:

CHILDHOOD AND ADOLESCENCE

I. LEARNING OBJECTIVES

Study of this chapter should enable the student to:

1. Know what methods have been used to learn about early sexuality, and describe some of the drawbacks of these methods.

2. Be aware of recent changes in our assumptions about how and when sexuality develops.

3. Indicate the major researchers and how they contributed to our knowledge of this area.

4. Compare and contrast human sexual behavior in infancy, early childhood, preadolescence, and adolescence.

5. Indicate the ages at which the following behaviors normally begin to appear in the typical child: "absent-minded" masturbation, systematic masturbation, orgasm, ejaculation, awareness of gender differences in the genitals, heterosexual play, heterosexual and homosexual behavior, kissing games, and first intercourse.

6. Trace the development of sexual knowledge and interest in young children.

7. Describe changes in our sexual attitudes and behavior over the past thirty years.

8. Compare male/female responses to first intercourse.

9. Describe Reiss' typology of standards for premarital sex.

10. Indicate adolescents' motives for having premarital sex.

11. Briefly describe Erikson's eight stages of psychosexual development.

12. Indicate ways in which sexuality is related to human psychosocial development.

13. Specify how the following people have increased our understanding of early sexual development: Kinsey, Hunt, Bell, Reiss, and Sorensen.

14. Describe the research on cohabitation in college, including differences found between cohabitants and noncohabitants.

II. CHAPTER AT A GLANCE

Introduction (p. 232): Describes changes in our notions about when sexuality develops.

Data Sources (pp. 232-233): Discusses methods and some of their drawbacks.

Infancy (0 to 2 years) (pp. 233-235)
    Masturbation
    Infant-Infant Sexual Encounters
    Nongenital Sensual Experiences: Discusses feeding and cuddling.
    Knowing About Boy-Girl Differences

Early Childhood (3 to 7 years) (pp. 235-237)
    Masturbation
    Heterosexual Behavior
    Homosexual Behavior
    Sex Knowledge and Interests

Preadolescence (8 to 12 years) (pp. 237-240)
    Masturbation
    Heterosexual Behavior
    Homosexual Behavior
    Dating
    Sexual Values

Adolescence (13 to 19 years) (pp. 240-242)
    Masturbation
        Attitudes toward masturbation
    Heterosexual Behavior
    Homosexual Behavior

Premarital Sex (pp. 242-250)
    How Many People Have Premarital Sex?
    First Intercourse
    Sex With a Prostitute
    Techniques in Premarital Sex
    Attitudes Toward Premarital Sex: Uses Reiss' typology.
    Motives for Having Premarital Sex
    Rampant Promiscuity? Describes data which lead to a negative answer.
    Dating, Going Steady, Getting Engaged
    Conflicts: Involving parents and children, as well as conflicts between attitudes and behavior.

How Sexuality Aids in Psychosexual Development (pp. 250-252): Reviews Erikson's stages and Bell's developmental tasks.

Summary (pp. 252-253)

Suggestions for Further Reading (p. 253)

Focuses:

Profile of the Sexual Behavior and Attitudes of the Students in a University Course in Human Sexuality (pp. 244-245)

Cohabiting in College: Going Very Steady (pp. 250-251)

III. GLOSSARY

cohabitation. Living together.

premarital intercourse. Intercourse before marriage.

promiscuous. A term used to refer to someone who engages in sexual activity with many different people.

sexual identity. A person's sense of his or her own sexual nature, whether heterosexual, homosexual, or bisexual.

IV. AUDIO-VISUAL AIDS

Movies:

Would you kiss a naked man? Perennial, #1048, 20 min., color, $275/$28. Explores teenage attitudes and behaviors toward sexuality and morality. Focuses on sexual role playing, values clarification, sexual games people play, the concept of "love", the search for commitment, peer group influences, parent-child relationships, nudity, and male/female virginity. Contains a short, relatively modest nude scene.

Adolescent sexual conflict. CRM-McGraw-Hill, 14 min., color, $195/$20. Teenaged couple engage in a heated argument about the extent of their sexual involvement.

Achieving sexual maturity. This film has been described in Ch. 3, but may be used appropriately here if students have not yet seen it.

Tapes:

Sexual development. Norton, #340058, 60 min., $14. Presents various theories of sexual development: Freudian, social learning, cognitive development, and the psychosexual bias maturational interaction theory. Heterosexuality and homosexuality, and masculinity and femininity are discussed in light of these different theories, as are prenatal physiological occurrences which affect subsequent sexual development.

Harold T. Christensen—Cultures and Sexual Intimacy. Norton, #350134, 25 min., $14. Premarital sexual behavior is described in three different cultures.

V. DEMONSTRATIONS OR GROUP DISCUSSION

Sharing experiences of childhood sexuality. The purpose of this exercise is to help students recall their childhood experiences of sexuality and to share these with other students.

Distribute the sentence completion form below to students for individual completion. After completion, divide the class into groups of 6-8 and have the students share and discuss their responses. If you feel that students might be threatened by revealing their own responses, anonymity can be preserved by collecting and randomly redistributing the responses, and having students read the response that is handed to them.

Finally, students can discuss what they might want to do to help their own children over the difficult parts of some of these experiences. They might also discuss which areas, if any, involve issues for which they feel it is "best to leave well enough alone."

SENTENCE COMPLETION TASK

1. When I was a kid, my parents told me _____
_____ about sex.

2. The first time I saw the genitals of a member of the opposite gender, _____.

3. I remember playing "doctor" _____.

4. The first time I heard about sexual intercourse, _____
_____.

5. The first time I felt sexually aroused, _____
_____.

6. The first time I masturbated, _____
_____.

VI. EVALUATION MATERIALS

Essay or research questions

1. Critically evaluate the research methods used to gather our information about childhood and adolescent sexuality. What kinds of data are we lacking? Can you think of any practical and ethical ways to obtain these data? (See pp. 232-233 for discussion of methods and their limitations.)

2. Based on your awareness of the research on the behavior, describe the masturbatory behavior you might expect in your male or female child from infancy through adolescence. Should you decide to become a parent, what kinds of responses to masturbation do you think you could give to be most helpful to your child's development? (See pp. 233, 235, 237, 240-241, 244 for description of typical masturbatory behavior at various ages.)

3. It has been claimed that today's young people are lacking any standards and are engaged in casual, promiscuous sex. Do the available data support this claim? Describe the data (or observations) on which you base your opinion. (See pp. 248-249 for discussion of data relevant to the claim that casual sex is on the increase.)

4. Sexuality is related to a number of developmental tasks. Select one of Erikson's 8 crises or one of the four tasks described by Bell and describe how the handling of one's sexuality may retard or aid in the development toward adult maturity. You may use a friend (or yourself) to provide an example, if you wish. (See pp. 250-252 for Erikson's and Bell's ideas.)

Multiple choice

1. Which of the following kinds of data have NOT been gathered regarding childhood sexuality? *a. systematic direct observation; b. interviews with adults about their childhood sexual development; c. interviews with children about their sexuality; d. neither a nor c have been used; e. none of the above have been used. (p. 233)

2. Cross-cultural research indicates that humans progress from absent-minded fingering of their genitals to systematic masturbation: a. during infancy; b. at 3-5 years of age; *c. at 6-8 years of age; d. at 10-12 years of age. (pp. 233-234)

3. Males are incapable of ___ before puberty. a. erection; *b. ejaculation; c. orgasm; d. both b & c. (p. 234)

4. Infants who masturbate: a. are likely to become hypersexual in adolescence; b. are likely to become hyposexual in adolescence; *c. are exhibiting normal sexual expression; d. need to have their genitals cleansed more thoroughly. (p. 234)

5. Sex play with members of one's own gender is more likely than sex play with members of the other gender during: a. infancy; b. early childhood; c. late childhood; d. preadolescence; *e. both c & d. (p. 236)

6. In preadolescence, most information about masturbation: a. is obtained from peers; b. is obtained accidently through self-discovery; *c. is obtained from peers by boys and from self-discovery by girls; d. is obtained from peers by girls and from self-discovery by boys. (p. 238)

7. According to data gathered in the 1960's from several studies, ___ engage in homosexual play during preadolescence. a. a majority of males and females; b. a minority of males and females; *c. a majority of males and a minority of females; d. a majority of females and a minority of males. (p. 239)

8. Marriage tends to be seen as a prerequisite for sexual intercourse by: *a. preadolescents; b. adolescents; c. both a & b; d. neither a nor b. (p. 240)

9. Hyde suggests that the heightened sexuality of puberty may be caused by: a. awareness of bodily changes; b. rises in levels of sex hormones; c. increased cultural emphasis on sex; d. rehearsal for adult roles; *e. all of the above. (p. 240)

10. After six months of heterosexual abstinance, John and Mary began to have sexual intercourse. Based on the data regarding the relationship between masturbation and heterosexual activity, it is likely that frequency of masturbation: a. will increase for John, but decrease for Mary; *b. will increase for Mary, but decrease for John; c. will increase for both John and Mary; d. will decrease for both John and Mary; e. none of the above; there are no studies of the relationship between masturbation and heterosexual activity. (p. 241)

11. Most adolescents have their first homosexual act with: a. a person younger than they are; *b. a person their own age; c. an older teenager; d. an adult; e. both c & d. (p. 242)

12. According to the Sorensen report, ___ attached less significance to first intercourse than ___ did. a. males, females; *b. females, males; c. neither a nor b; there were no gender differences in the significance attached to first intercourse; d. none of the above; no research has been conducted on the significance attached to first intercourse. (p. 246)

13. Compared to thirty years ago, a ___ percentage of men have sex
    with prostitutes and these men tend to have contacts with a ___
    number of prostitutes. *a. smaller, smaller; b. larger, larger;
    c. smaller, larger; d. larger, smaller. (p. 246)

14. Which of the following occurs with less frequency now than it
    did thirty years ago? a. premarital sex; b. fellatio; c. cunnil-
    ingus; *d. use of prostitutes. (p. 246)

15. The wives of men who used prostitutes prior to marriage tend to
    obtain orgasm ___ than the wives of men who have not used pro-
    stitutes. a. earlier, and with greater frequency; b. later, and
    with less frequency; c. later, but with greater frequency;
    d. earlier, and with greater frequency, but only if expensive
    prostitutes were used; *e. none of the above; Hyde reports no
    studies of the relationship between prostitute use and sexual
    satisfaction of spouses. (p. 246)

16. Until recent years in the U.S., the standard regarding premarital
    sex, as described by Reiss, has involved ___. *a. abstinence or
    the double standard; b. permissiveness with affection; c. per-
    missiveness without affection; d. sex for recreation. (p. 247)

17. At the present, the U.S. standard regarding premarital sex, as
    described by Reiss, involves ___. a. abstinence or the double
    standard; *b. permissiveness with affection; c. permissiveness
    without affection; d. sex for recreation. (p. 247)

18. ___ is NOT among the common motives adolescents have given as
    their reasons for having premarital sex. a. need for new
    experiences; b. desire to escape from tension; *c. physical
    pleasure; d. means of communication. (pp. 247-248)

19. In Hunt's sample, the majority of those women engaging in pre-
    marital sex did so with ___ partner(s). *a. one; b. two;
    c. three; d. four; e. five. (pp. 248-249)

20. In the Cornell study of cohabitation in college, cohabitants
    ___ noncohabitants. a. did not differ in their academic per-
    formance from; b. were less interested in eventual marriage
    than; c. did not differ in the desire for eventual marriage
    from; d. both a & b; *e. both a & c. (p. 250)

21. According to Erikson's theory of psychosocial development, a
    5-year old who masturbates: a. is expressing autonomy and ini-
    tiative; b. feels shame and guilt; c. feels isolation; *d. both
    a & b; which the child experiences depends on parental reac-
    tions to the masturbation. (p. 250)

<u>True/False</u>

1. In recent years, scientists have departed from the notion that crucial aspects of human and sexual development all occur in childhood and now believe that such development occurs throughout the life span (T, p. 232).

2. Males are capable of erections from birth onward (T, p. 233).

3. Children with problematic relationships with their mothers are more likely to masturbate than children with optimal relationships with their mothers (F, p. 234).

4. Awareness of gender differences in the genitals and in urination positions don't begin to appear until about the age of 2 to $2\frac{1}{2}$ (T, p. 235).

5. Modesty about masturbation (that is, engaging in the behavior only in private) appears to be innate, as children avoid genital fingering when others are present, even in infancy (F, p. 235).

6. All infants enjoy cuddling; differences in the extent to which they want physical contact do not appear until early childhood (F, pp. 234-235).

7. The available data suggest that infants are more likely to engage in masturbation than are children during early childhood (T, pp. 234-235).

8. Generally, children do not develop principles of modesty and privacy until the ages of 10 to 12 (F, p. 237).

9. Consistent with other gender differences in development, girls begin masturbating at an earlier age than boys do (F, p. 237).

10. Nearly twice as many girls indicated that they had masturbated to orgasm by age 13 in Hunt's sample than did so in Kinsey's sample (T, p. 238).

11. Although preadolescent homosexual behavior is unrelated to adult homosexual preferences, adolescents who engage in homosexual behavior tend to prefer homosexual behavior in adulthood (F, p. 241).

12. Presently, almost all males, and at least two-third of all females, engage in premarital sex (T, p. 243).

13. Sorensen's study found that males, compared to females, were twice as likely to report positive reactions such as feelings of maturity and joy after first intercourse (T, p. 246).

14. In the past thirty years, the percentage of males having first intercourse with a prostitute has increased (F, p. 246).

15. Most married women in Kinsey's (1953) sample who engaged in premarital sex expressed regret at having done so (F, p. 249).

16. Prior to living together, all cohabitants in the Cornell study had been engaging in premarital sex with their partner on a fairly regular basis (F, pp. 250-251).

17. "Lack of opportunity" rather than "ethical standards" was a more frequent reason given by noncohabitants for their living arrangements in the Cornell study of college cohabitation (T, p. 251).

18. Cohabitants in the Cornell study generally described their relationship as a "trial marriage" (F, p. 251).

CHAPTER 11: SEXUALITY AND

THE LIFE CYCLE: ADULTHOOD

I. LEARNING OBJECTIVES

Study of this chapter should enable the student to:

1. Specify the percentage of people who marry and the average frequency with which they have marital sex.

2. Indicate several of the problems with using average frequencies in evaluating one's own sexual behavior.

3. Compare the Westoff study with the studies by Hunt and Kinsey with respect to their findings regarding frequency of marital sex.

4. Describe changes in techniques used in marital sex in the last few generations.

5. Describe the negotiation process in marital intercourse.

6. Specify the incidence of masturbation in marriage.

7. Indicate the extent to which marital sex appears to be satisfying to couples, and describe changes in satisfaction which occur over the course of marriage.

8. Describe the influence on sexual frequency of both spouses being employed outside the home.

9. Define the different kinds of extramarital sex and indicate the extent to which people engage in it and the attitudes toward it in the United States.

10. Compare the degree of sexual satisfaction of partners in each of the five different types of successful marriage.

11. Describe the practice of swinging and the typical swinger.

12. Compare the sexual lives of males and females who have never been married, are divorced, or are widowed.

13. Describe the physical and psychological effects of aging on sexuality and the frequency with which the elderly have intercourse.

14. Specify the ways in which Cuber, Westoff, Hunt, Kinsey, and Masters & Johnson have contributed to our knowledge in this area.

II. CHAPTER AT A GLANCE

Introduction (p. 256)

Marital Sex (pp. 256-261)
    Frequency of Marital Sex
    Techniques in Marital Sex:
        Negotiations: Describes Gagnon's concepts of sexual scripts
           and negotiation regarding intercourse.
    Masturbation in Marriage
    Attitudes Toward, and Satisfaction With, Marital Sex
    Sexual Patterns in Marriage: Describes different patterns involv-
       ing both increasing and decreasing boredom with marital sex.
    Sex and the Two-Career Family: Notes that career women have the
       highest frequency of marital intercourse.

Extramarital Sex (pp. 261-266)
    How Many People Engage in Extramaterial Sex?
    Attitudes toward Extramarital Sex
    Consensual Extramarital Sex
        Open marriage: Based on the O'Neill's notions.
        Swinging: Describes Bartell's research.

Sex and the Single Person (pp. 266-267)
    The Never-Married
    The Divorced and Widowed
        Divorced and widowed women
        Divorced and widowed men

Sex and the Senior Citizen (pp. 267-272)
    Sexual Behavior of the Elderly
    Physical Changes
        Changes in the female
        Changes in the male
    Psychological Factors

Summary (pp. 272-273)

Suggestions for Further Reading (p. 273)

Focus:

    Sex in Five Types of Marriage (p. 262) Based on Cuber's typology.

III. GLOSSARY

    adultery. Sexual intercourse between a married person and some-
      one other than his or her spouse.

    extramarital sex. Sexual activity by a married person with some-
      one other than his or her spouse.

hysterectomy. Surgical removal of the uterus.

swinging. An exchange of sex partners among married couples.

IV. AUDIO-VISUAL AIDS

Movies:

A Ripple of Time. Multi Media, 24 min., color, $300/$50. A 50-
    year old woman and a 63-year-old man engage in a variety of
    sexual practices including intercourse, mouth-genital stimu-
    lation, and the use of a vibrator. The woman has several
    orgasms. The tenderness and technique they display are about
    the best of any sex films. The woman discusses her feelings
    of losing her sexuality when she was 40. Good for use in dis-
    cussion on sexuality and aging.

Not together now: End of a marriage. Polymorph, 25 min., color,
    $325/$30. A now-separated couple discuss their feelings about
    marriage, their children, their jobs, and their separation.
    Helpful as an aid to discussion of the realities of marriage,
    and it avoids taking a "who is to blame?" position.

Young marriage. CRM McGraw-Hill, #106670-5, 14 min., color,
    $195/$20. Shows some problems which occur in early marriage.

Tapes:

The marrieds. Norton, #340244, 60 min., $14. Discusses four
    major types of marital relationships including interdependent,
    dominance and submissive, mutually agressive, and independent
    or open. Ramifications of each life style are considered in
    terms of their sexual and social activities.

The non-marrieds. Norton, #340260, 60 min., $14. Interacting
    views from "never-been marrieds" and divorced or widowed per-
    sons regarding their sexual expectations, problems, and advan-
    tages. The future of the non-married condition in our society
    is reviewed.

V. DEMONSTRATIONS OR GROUP DISCUSSION

A. Guest speaker on sex and the elderly. If you have a local
branch of the Gray Panthers or any other senior citizens group, ask
someone from the group to come to speak to the class.

B. Guest speaker from Parents Without Partners. A member of this
group may be willing to discuss some of the difficulties faced by
divorced and widowed parents in dealing with their desires for social

and sexual contact in the context of having primary responsibility for raising their children.

C. Free association exercise. The purpose of this exercise is for students to consider their own attitudes about certain aspects of sexuality in such a way that they are not embarrassed if they do hold some stereotyped views. Each student should receive a piece of paper that has a diagram like this on it:

_____

_____

_____

_____

_____

_____

Each student should complete the form individually. Have them write the word to be discussed on the line at the left. Two particularly appropriate topics for this chapter would be extramarital sex and sex for old people. Students should then write, as rapidly as possible, their free associations with the phrase at the left, not thinking too long about any particular response. After that, they should circle the 2 or 3 they feel are most important, and to the right of those, elaborate a bit more about them. In groups of 6-8, students may then discuss their responses. If the instructor feels that anonymity is important, the responses may be collected in a pile and redistributed randomly. Note that this exercise may be used with a number of other chapters like homosexuality or gender roles just by providing key stem words appropriate to the topic.

VI. EVALUATION MATERIALS

Essay or research questions

1. Cuber has described five different, but long-lasting marriages including the (1) conflict-habituated; (2) passive-congenial, (3) devitalized, (4) vital, and (5) total marriage. Try to describe couples you know who have been married at least five years who fit into two of the five patterns. Why have you placed them in the category you've chosen? Finally, describe the pattern you think you would find most satisfying for you and indicate why you choose it over the others. (See p. 262 for Cuber's typology.)

2. Select an elderly married couple you know and describe their sex
life (intercourse, masturbation). Indicate the extent to which
their sexual activity is likely to be impaired by aging (based on
the research). Try to imagine yourself in your 70's, and describe
your sex life at that age. What can you do to increase the likelihood of a long and vibrant sex life? (See pp. 269-272 for description of effect of aging on sexuality.)

Multiple choice

1. In the U.S. approximately ___ marry. a. 60-70%; b. 70-80%;
    *c. 80-90%; d. 90-100%. (p. 256)

2. The best evidence of an increase in the frequency of marital
    intercourse in recent years has been provided by ___'s data.
    *a. Westoff; b. Hunt, C. Masters & Johnson; d. Kinsey;
    e. Sorensen. (p. 257)

3. Masturbation by married people: a. is the result of sexual
    problems; b. is quite normal; c. may evoke guilt; d. is almost
    always due to husband/wife differences in how often they want
    sex; *e. both b & c. (p. 258)

4. Women in the ___ age group report the greatest satisfaction with
    marital sex. a. under 25; b. 25-34; *c. 35-44; d. 45-54.
    (p. 259)

5. Comedians often make jokes about wives wishing to avoid ("I have
    a headache!") marital sex. To what extent are these jokes con-
    sistent with the evidence? a. quite consistent as the majority
    of women report wishing marital sex were less frequent; b. some-
    what consistent as a large minority wish marital sex were less
    frequent; c. somewhat inconsistent, as only about a third wish
    marital sex were less frequent; *d. very inconsistent as less
    than 5% wish marital sex were less frequent. (p. 260)

6. Regarding the frequency of marital sex, the majority of men and
    women: *a. report that its about right; b. wish it were more
    frequent; c. wish it were less frequent; d. wish it were more
    frequent while they are in their twenties, but less frequent
    when they are in their thirties. (p. 260)

7. It has been claimed that the loss of strong sex role norms will
    decrease interest in heterosexual relations. The data indicate
    that couples in ___ report more satisfaction, in ___ that claim.
    a. highly segregated role relationships, support of; *b. joint
    role relationships, contrast with; c. neither of the above; the
    kind of relationship appears to be unrelated to sexual satisfac-
    tion. (p. 261)

8. The highest frequency of intercourse occurs among: a. house-wives; b. women who work part time mainly for money; c. women who work full time mainly for money; *d. career-motivated working women. (p. 261)

9. ___ extramarital sex occurs least frequently in our society. a. clandestine; *b. consensual; c. ambiguous; d. adulterous. (p. 261)

10. Hunt found that a greater percentage of women in the ___ age group had engaged in extramarital sex than in any other age group. *a. under 25; b. 25-34; c. 35-44; d. 45-54; e. 55 and over. (p. 263)

11. Extramarital sex by ___ is more common now than in Kinsey's time. *a. women under 25; b. men under 25; c. women aged 25-35; d. men aged 25-35; e. all of the above. (p. 263)

12. For couples who engage in swinging, the most common way to find partners is to: *a. advertise in magazines and newspapers; b. convert nonswinging couples; c. go to swingers' bars; d. join swingers' organizations; e. none of these; we have very little information on the behavior of swingers. (p. 265)

13. In "open swinging," the two couples may have intercourse in the same room: a. quite frequently including sex between the two men; *b. quite frequently including sex between the two women; c. but rarely do the two men or the two women engage in homosexual behavior with each other; d. quite frequently involving homosexual behavior between the two men and the two women. (p. 265)

14. Swingers usually engage in swinging about: a. twice a week; b. once a week; *c. once every two weeks; d. once a month. (p. 265)

15. When divorced and widowed women of the same age are compared: a. widowed women are more likely to engage in postmarital sex, perhaps because they are less bitter than divorced women; b. widowed women are as likely to engage in postmarital sex; *c. widowed women are less likely to engage in postmarital sex; d. none of the above; the postmarital sexual behavior of widows has not been studied. (p. 267)

16. Which of these groups are least likely to engage in postmarital sex? a. divorced men; b. divorced women; c. widowed men; *d. widowed women; e. widowed men and women. (p. 267)

17. When an aging couple stops engaging in intercourse: a. both wives and husbands report that the wife is the cause; *b. both wives and husbands report that the husband is the cause;

117

c. husbands blame wives and wives blame husbands; d. both report that it was by mutual consent. (pp. 268-269)

18. In an elderly woman, the vagina ___ in length and width.
a. expands; *b. shrinks; c. is about the same as it was when she was in her twenties; d. none of the above; Hyde reports no data on the effect of aging on vaginal length and width. (p. 269)

19. Masters and Johnson's research indicates that the physical effect of aging on sexuality are less severe in women who have: a. had intercourse regularly once or twice a week; b. masturbated regularly; c. received injections of progesterone; d. all of the above; *e. both a & b. (p. 270)

20. Marion's husband usually travels in connection with his job for most of the week. She enjoys masturbating during his absence, but really relishes their regular Sunday afternoon love-making. She is in the midst of menopause when she learns that she must have a hysterectomy. The operation will probably: a. reduce her interest in sex; b. reduce her ability to have orgasm through masturbation; c. reduce her ability to have orgasm during sexual intercourse; *d. leave her sexual and orgasm capacity unaffected as long as her ovaries are not removed; e. leave her sexual and orgasm capacity unaffected even if her ovaries are removed. (p. 270)

21. With aging: a. a woman's estrogen levels decline gradually, but a man's testosterone levels remain unaffected; b. a man's testosterone levels decline gradually, but a woman's estrogen levels remain unaffected; *c. both a woman's estrogen levels and a man's testosterone levels gradually decline; d. the hormone levels of both men and women remain unaffected. (pp. 269-270)

22. Among the physical influences of aging on men: a. is a decrease in the speed of erection; b. is a decrease in the frequency of morning erections; c. is an increase in the length of the refractory period; d. is a decrease in testosterone production; *e. all of the above. (p. 270)

23. As a man ages, he has: a. less control over ejaculation; b. less ejaculate; c. more control over ejaculation; d. both a & b; *e. both b & c. (p. 270)

24. Removal of the prostate: *a. reduces the volume of the ejaculate; b. causes impotence; c. decreases orgasmic capacity; d. all of the above. (p. 271)

25. George has had a heart attack and is worried about resuming sexual relations with his wife. In general: a. he should avoid any sort of arousal; b. he should abstain from sex, as the activity of intercourse may precipitate another attack; c. he

may engage in love-making to satisfy his wife, but should avoid orgasm as it may precipitate an attack; *d. he may resume sex and orgasm as the benefits for his health outweigh any dangers. (p. 271)

True/False

1. Although premarital sex is more common now than several generations ago, the frequency of marital sex has not increased (F, p. 256).

2. Married couples over 55 have intercourse an average of once a week (T, p. 256).

3. About 8 to 12% of married couples in their twenties report that they do not have intercourse at all (T, p. 256).

4. In Kinsey's sample, the average man reached orgasm about ten minutes after insertion (F, p. 257).

5. The majority of married couples in Hunt's sample engaged in oral sex (T, p. 258).

6. The older the person, the greater the satisfaction he/she reports from marital sex (F, p. 259).

7. In general, men report somewhat more satisfaction with marital sex than do women (T, p. 259).

8. Although a minority of women appear to engage in extramarital sex, the majority of those who do have between 6 and 10 partners (F, p. 263).

9. People appear to be considerably more tolerant of extramarital sex now than they were several decades ago (F, p. 263).

10. A majority of both men and women report engaging in extramarital sex at least once (F, p. 263).

11. Approximately half of all males but considerably fewer females report engaging in extramarital sex (T, p. 263).

12. When a couple swings with just one other person, that person is generally female (T, p. 265).

13. When a couple finds another couple to swing with, they generally continue to meet periodically for sex over a period of six months to a year (F, p. 265).

14. Most swingers tend to be politically conservative (T, p. 265).

15. Most swingers tend to be politically liberal (F, p. 265).

16. Women who engage in postmarital sex are more likely to have multiple partners than women who engage in premarital sex (T, p. 267).

17. Women have orgasm more frequently in postmarital sex than they did in marital sex (T, p. 267).

18. Both divorced and widowed women who engage in postmarital sex do so within a year of the divorce or death (T, p. 267).

19. Cessation of sexual intercourse by an aging couple is generally due to the husband rather than the wife (T, p. 269).

20. As a woman ages, her physical capacity for orgasm diminishes (F, p. 269).

21. The effect of aging and a decrease in testosterone production is to increase the time a man takes to become erect (T, p. 270).

22. Both men and women have a longer refractory period as they get older (F, p. 270).

23. During the twenty to thirty years following menopause, women gradually become physically incapable of multiple orgasm (F, p. 270).

24. Morton is 78 and has married a 35 year old woman. When she becomes pregnant, he assumes she's been "fooling around" because he believes he's too old to father a child. His belief is ___ (F, p. 270).

25. The most important factor in maintaining sexual capacity throughout the life span is engaging in sex regularly (T, p. 272).

CHAPTER 12: GENDER ROLES

I. LEARNING OBJECTIVES

Study of this chapter should enable the student to:

1. Define gender roles and stereotypes, and indicate the advantages and disadvantages of stereotypes.

2. Describe the socialization process and indicate how socializing agents influence the development of adult gender roles.

3. Specify the stereotypes regarding traits considered desirable from women versus men, and know what is meant by nonconscious ideologies of gender roles.

4. Describe the gender differences identified by researchers in each of the developmental periods across the life span.

5. Discuss Horner's concepts of femininity-achievement incompatibility and ambivalence, describe the research relevant to these concepts, and the double-bind experienced by some working adult women.

6. Indicate the effect of motherhood, the "empty-nest syndrome," and widowhood on career women vs. housewives throughout adulthood.

7. Discuss the stresses imposed by gender role expectations on men during adulthood and old age.

8. Describe gender differences in personality and kind of abilities.

9. Relate the differences in communication styles between men and women to potential difficulties in their heterosexual relations with one another.

10. Specify those stereotypic gender differences which have been validated by research (that is, found to be "real" differences) and indicate possible causes of these differences.

11. Describe the possible effects of gender roles regarding aggressiveness, arousal, and emotionality on male-female sexual interaction.

12. Define "androgyny" and describe the research on it, and indicate your opinion of the potential effect of androgynous identification on heterosexual interaction.

13. Describe the contributions of Broverman, Bem, Horner, and Maccoby & Jacklin to our understanding of this area.

II. CHAPTER AT A GLANCE

<u>Introduction</u> (p. 276): Notes the difficulty we have interacting with someone if we don't know their gender.

<u>Gender Roles and Stereotypes</u> (pp. 276-278): Defines these terms, discusses their advantages and disadvantages and describes the socialization process and its agents.

<u>Growing Up Female</u> (pp. 279-284)
    <u>Stereotypes About Women</u>: Describes Broverman, et al.'s research.
    <u>Infancy and Early Childhood</u>: Notes gender differences in aggressiveness, toy preference and developmental speed.
    <u>Childhood</u>: Discusses differences in scholastic achievement and amount of freedom regarding gender roles.
    <u>Adolescence</u>: Reviews Horner's research.
    <u>Adulthood</u>: Describes employment figures and double-binds experienced by adult working women.
    <u>Middle and Old Age</u>: Notes the effects of empty-nest syndrome, widowhood, menopause, and loss of attractiveness on women; compares the adjustment of housewives and career women to these events.

<u>Growing Up Male</u> (pp. 284-287): The coverage in this section is parallel to Growing Up Female.
    <u>Stereotypes About Men</u>
    <u>Infancy and Early Childhood</u>
    <u>Childhood</u>
    <u>Adolescence</u>
    <u>Adulthood</u>
    <u>Middle and Old Age</u>

<u>Male-Female Psychological Differences</u> (pp. 287-290)
    <u>Personality</u>: Reviews difference in aggressiveness and self-esteem.
    <u>Abilities</u>
    <u>Communication Styles</u>: Discusses differences in verbal precision, talking time, self-disclosure, and non-verbal behavior and discusses the implications of these differences for heterosexual interaction.
    <u>Gender Similarities</u>: Notes that similarity rather than difference is the rule.
    <u>Stereotypes, Real Differences, and the Nature-Nuture Issue</u>

<u>Impact of Gender Roles on Sexuality</u> (pp. 290-291)
    <u>Aggressive versus Passive</u>
    <u>Aroused versus Unaroused</u>
    <u>Emotional versus Unemotional</u>

<u>A New Trend: Androgyny</u> (pp. 292-293): Describes the concept, Bem's measure of it and the research conducted to date.

Summary (pp. 293-294)

Suggestions for Further Reading (p. 294)

Focus:

Nonconscious Ideologies of Gender Roles (pp. 280-281)
(Sandra & Daryl Bem's 1970 essay).

III. GLOSSARY

androgyny. Having both feminine and masculine characteristics.

IV. AUDIO-VISUAL AIDS

Movies:

Self-identity/Sex roles. CRM McGraw-Hill, 16 min., color, $195/
$20. Three related females with three different lifestyles
begin to understand each other.

Women: The hand that cradles the rock. Document, 20 min., color,
$300/$40. Presents women holding both feminist and traditional
views of women's roles, marriage, and child rearing. Good
for initiation of discussion of changing sex roles.

Sex role development. CRM McGraw-Hill, 23 min., color, $295/$35.
Examines methods of eliminating sexual stereotyping of young-
sters.

V. DEMONSTRATIONS OR GROUP DISCUSSION

A. Guest Speaker. If there are male liberation or female liberation groups in your area, ask them to provide a speaker on conscious-
ness-raising regarding sex roles and sexuality.

B. Gender Reversal Exercise. This exercise helps students become
aware of the nature of some of the gender-role stereotypes present
in our culture, and particularly of some of their more subtle aspects.
Have each student bring in an article or ad from a newspaper
or magazine. They should switch the genders throughout; that is,
every time it says "he" switch it to "she", every time it says
Jennifer, switch it to John. Have students read or show their contributions, first in the original, and then with genders reversed.
Have the class discuss what seems peculiar or even humorous about
the excerpt when the genders are switched, and what that reveals
about gender-role assumptions in our culture. They should pay particular attention to subtle aspects. For example, in many photos or

pictorial ads, the women's heads are placed lower than the men's, and it looks strange when they are reversed.

Some of the best examples for this course will be "sexual sell" advertising--for example, a woman selling a mattress by reclining seductively on it. The class can then also discuss how advertising uses sex to sell products.

Instructors wanting further exercises in this area should consult Beyond Sex Roles, by Alice G. Sargent (New York: West Publishing Co., 1977), which has many excellent ideas.

C. Questioning the other gender. Divide students into small same-sexed groups and ask them to generate and write down questions they have for the opposite sex about their feelings about dating, sexual behavior, marital and parental behavior. Have males give their questions to female groups and vice versa. After groups have answered each other's questions, attempt to help them distinguish between those questions having to do with stereotypic gender roles versus those questions based on actual sex differences. This exercise provides a good vehicle for talking about value judgments versus factual information.

VI. EVALUATION MATERIALS

Essay or research questions

1. What are the agents of sex role socialization in our society and how are role expectations transmitted? Which ones had the strongest influence on your development, and why? (See pp. 277-278.)

2. Describe the way in which several gender role stereotypes might have negative effects on heterosexual interaction. To what extent do you feel that these stereotypes have influenced your interaction with the other gender, and in what ways have they done so. (See pp. 290-291.)

3. Hyde refers to several double-binds which exist for some females in our culture. Describe one of these and include the relevant research on the issue. Do you think there are some double-binds for men? If not, why not, and if so, what are they. (See pp. 282-283 for the double-binds. Double-binds for males might include the pressure from the culture to be non-emotional versus the pressure from partners to be more expressive of their emotionality, etc.)

Multiple choice

1. Stereotypes: a. give us some information in situations in which we would otherwise have no information; b. may lead to false assumptions about people; c. tend to restrict people's opportunities; *d. all of the above; e. both b & c. (pp. 276-277)

2. The gender role socialization process has been completed by the time an individual is ___ years of age. a. 5; b. 9; c. 15; d. 19; *e. none of the above; it continues into adulthood. (p. 277)

3. In our culture, a stereotypic feminine trait which is not valued is: a. expressiveness; b. lack of competitiveness; c. warmth; d. emotionality; *e. both b & d. (p. 279)

4. By the age of two, girls ___ than boys. a. are less aggressive; b. have different toy preferences; c. have a greater preference for dolls and sewing; d. are developmentally more mature in their nervous system, etc; *e. all of the above (p. 279)

5. Sex differences existing in infancy and early childhood include all but one of the following. Which has not been found? a. aggression; b. toy preference; *c. intelligence; d. speed of physical development. (p. 279)

6. The transmission of gender role expectations through nonconscious ideologies has been described by: a. Broverman, et al.; b. Maccoby & Jacklin; c. Horner; d. Money; *e. Bem & Bem. (p. 280)

7. All but one of the following are examples of nonconscious ideologies. Which one is not? a. sexist jokes; *b. discriminatory laws; c. Biblical passages regarding gender roles; d. sexist cartoons; e. both b & c. (pp. 280-281)

8. Hyde suggested that pressures to conform to gender roles may be stronger during ___ than at any other stage in life. a. infancy; b. childhood; *c. adolescence; d. adulthood; e. middle age. (p. 282)

9. Which of these gender differences appear well before adolescence? a. spatial ability; *b. aggressiveness; c. grip strength; d. speed in the 100-yard dash; e. all of the above. (p. 282)

10. Mothers who combine the wife/mother role with a career appear to be happier than mothers who remain in the home: a. in their mid-20's; *b. in their mid-40's; c. both of the above; d. neither of the above. (p. 284)

11. Boys have more adjustment problems in elementary school than girls do probably because, according to Hyde: a. most elementary teachers are female; b. boys lag behind girls developmentally; c. boys tend to be more aggressive; d. both b & c; *e. all of the above. (p. 285)

12. Compared to men, women: a. are more physically aggressive; b. are more verbally aggressive; c. engage in more fantasy aggression; d. both b & c; *e. none of the above. (p. 287)

13. On the whole, males do not differ from females with respect to: a. aggressiveness; b. self-esteem; *c. general intelligence; d. both a & c; e. all of the above. (p. 287)

14. Males tend to excel over females in ___ ability. a. verbal; b. mathematical; c. spatial; *d. both b & c; e. all of the above. (p. 287)

15. In communicating, males, compared to females: a. enunciate more precisely; *b. spend more time talking; c. interrupt less; d. are more self-disclosing; e. all of the above. (pp. 288-289)

16. All but one of the following dimensions were described as gender role stereotypes which may have a negative impact on pleasure-able heterosexual interaction. Which was not included? a. aggressive/passive; b. aroused/unaroused; *c. strong/weak; d. emotional/unemotional. (pp. 290-291)

17. The term "androgynous" refers to: *a. the possession of both masculine and feminine traits; b. women who are overly masculine; c. men who are overly feminine; d. both b & c. (p. 292)

18. Research on androgyny is based on the assumption that: a. masculinity is the opposite of femininity; b. holding both masculine and feminine traits demonstrates sex role confusion; *c. healthy individuals may have both masculine and feminine traits; d. both a & b. (pp. 292-293)

19. Development of a pencil/paper test to measure androgyny was by: *a. Bem; b. Horner; c. Broverman; d. Maccoby & Jacklin. (p. 292)

20. Mary is a first semester freshman who is having a bad bout of homesickness. She shyly attempts to talk about it with several people in the student union, but not until she runs into Terry does she get a sympathetic response. Terry is probably: a. a "masculine" male; b. an anthropomorphic female; *c. androgynous; d. a "masculine" female; e. none of the above. (p. 293)

True/False

1. Gender role refers to existing sex differences in personality that have been found via research (F, p. 276).

2. The socialization of gender roles in our country began to be questioned when it was discovered that not all societies have gender roles (F, p. 278).

3. There tends to be more rigid adherence to gender role expectations among teenagers than among couples of retirement age (T, p. 278).

4. The expectations regarding how women versus men should behave regarding gender roles varies from culture to culture (T, p. 278).

5. Parents' tendency to treat boys and girls differently diminishes as children get older (F, p. 279).

6. Hyde suggests that girls appear to have more freedom than boys do with respect to conformity to gender roles during childhood (T, p. 282).

7. Girls tend to begin the late-adolescent process of adult identity formation earlier than boys do (F, p. 283).

8. By the mid-70's, a majority of women aged 20-55 held paying jobs (T, p. 283).

9. There is no evidence that the children of working mothers suffer more psychological damage than the children of non-working mothers (T, p. 283).

10. Females are more likely than males to have psychotherapy (T, p. 284).

11. In their 40's, women who are housewives have higher self-esteem than employed women (F, p. 284)

12. Career women are happier than housewives throughout the adult life span (F, p. 284).

13. Females tend to have more confidence in their abilities than do males (F, p. 287).

14. Consistent with their greater aggressiveness, males stand closer to other males when in public than females do to other females (F, p. 289).

15. Gender similarities (rather than gender differences) seem to be the rule, according to Hyde (T, p. 289).

16. Research has demonstrated that androgynous people are more likely to conform than feminine people (F, p. 293).

Matching

Match the following researchers with their contribution to our understanding of the impact of gender role expectations.

___ 1. Bem

___ 2. Broverman, et al.

___ 3. Horner

___ 4. Maccoby & Jacklin

___ 5. Hughes & Seligman

a. found that women talk more and interrupt more than men do.

b. developed and did research on "femininity-achievement incompatibility" and "fear of success."

c. constructed a pencil and paper measure of androgyny.

d. studied the stereotypes regarding gender roles held by people in the United States.

e. none of the above.

<u>Matching answer key</u>:   1. c; 2. d; 3. b; 4. e; 5. e.

CHAPTER 13:   FEMALE SEXUALITY AND MALE SEXUALITY

I. LEARNING OBJECTIVES

Study of this chapter should enable the student to:

1. Specify those differences in male and female sexuality which appear to be disappearing versus those which still appear.

2. Describe and evaluate the research regarding male and female response to erotica.

3. Describe the various explanations for gender differences in sexuality and evaluate the research in support of each of these explanations, indicating both Hyde's conclusion and your own.

4. Discuss the research regarding claims that (a) male impotence is increasing, and (b) women's liberation is the cause of that increase.

5. Evaluate Masters & Johnson's speculation that females may have stronger sex drives than males.

6. Indicate how notions of female sexuality, as presented in sex manuals, have changed over the past century.

7. Compare Hite's method and findings with those of Pietropinto and Simenauer.

8. Define the terms penile strain gauge and photoplethysmograph.

9. Specify the contributions to our understanding of gender differences in sexuality made by Heiman, Hite, Kaplan, Schmidt & Sigusch, Masters & Johnson, and Pietropinto & Simenauer.

II. CHAPTER AT A GLANCE

Introduction (p. 296)

Data on Male-Female Differences in Sexuality (pp. 296-301)
<u>Orgasm Consistency</u>: Females have had orgasm with less consistency
than men, but the difference is diminishing.
<u>Desire for Sex and Motives for Having Intercourse</u>: Females attach
more importance to "love" than males do.
<u>Masturbation</u>: Gender differences in incidence still exist.
<u>Arousal Response to Erotica</u>: Describes research by Schmidt &
Sigusch and by Heiman; concludes that gender differences
are disappearing.

Why the Differences (pp. 301-307): Need to explain gender differences in masturbation and orgasm consistency.
<u>Biological Factors</u>
    <u>Anatomy</u>
    <u>Hormones</u>
<u>Cultural Factors</u>
<u>Other Factors</u>: Men don't get pregnant, ineffective stimulation,
less training via masturbation.

Beyond the Young Adults (pp. 307-312): Discusses Kaplan's and
Reiss' ideas.

The Future (pp. 312-313)
<u>Gender Similarities</u>: Suggests that the trend toward diminishing
differences will continue.
<u>The "New Impotence"?</u> Gives opinion that male impotence can't be
blamed on female liberation.
<u>Greater Sex Drive in Women?</u> Discusses Masters & Johnson's specu-
lation, notes the paucity of research on male sexuality.

Summary (pp. 313-314)

Suggestions for Further Reading (p. 314)

Focuses:

<u>Different Equals Less: Female Sexuality in Recent Sex Manuals</u>
(pp. 302-303): Reviews suppositions in sex manuals from
1869-1969.

<u>Female Sexuality: The Hite Report; Male Sexuality: Beyond the
Male Myth</u> (pp. 308-311): The latter is a report of Pietropinto
& Simenauer's study.

III. GLOSSARY

The only problematic terms in this chapter are the two instruments used to measure arousal in Heiman's study, the penile strain gauge (male) and the photoplethysmograph (female). They are described and pictured on pages 299-300.

IV. AUDIO-VISUAL AIDS

Movies:

The Sexes: Breaking the barriers. Document, 18 min., color, $275/$40. Masters & Johnson discuss the need for education regarding male and female sexuality. "Sexploitation" and the pros and cons of industries ranging from show business to advertising are evaluated in terms of their effects on sexual attitudes and behavior.

Female Body Imagery. CMSS, #20, 33 min., color, $395/$75. A nude woman is placed before three mirrors and asked to examine every part of her body and comment on her likes, dislikes, and feelings about each part. Then she lies down and is asked to take an imaginary trip through the inside of her body, commenting on each area.

Male Body Imagery. CMSS, #21, 33 min., color, $395/$75. Very similar in format to Female Body Imagery, described above.

Becoming orgasmic: A sexual growth program for women. Focus, 52 min., color, $300/$50 for each film. This is a series of three films (Self-Discovery, Pleasuring, Sharing), designed for women who have had difficulty experiencing orgasm with a partner. Through a series of self-exploration exercises developed by Joseph LoPiccolo and W. C. Lobitz, women discover how to give themselves pleasure and eventually teach their partner what they have learned. Film 1 shows a woman exploring her genitals and discovering areas of her body that give her pleasure. She describes her fears and hesitations about what she is doing. Film 2 shows the woman experimenting with such techniques as the use of erotic literature, fantasy, orgasm triggers, vibrator, and body movement exercises. Feelings that can interfere with the ability to "let go" are discussed. Film 3 shows the woman pleasuring herself in the presence of her partner and then guiding him as he learns to please her effectively. Intercourse and concurrent manual stimulation with positions to facilitate it are depicted, and good communication is stressed throughout.

V. DEMONSTRATIONS OR GROUP DISCUSSION

A. Sex differences in sexuality exercise. You may want to begin this just before consideration of the material in chapter 13, to foster communication between males and females regarding the similarities and differences in their sexuality.

Part 1. Divide the class into two groups, one of all females and the other of all males. The task of each group is to define how the sexuality of the opposite sex differs from their own sexuality. For example, the female group will discuss male sexuality and how it differs from female sexuality (this will, of necessity, involve some defining of female sexuality). The groups should focus on the following list of questions (and any other relevant ones they may generate):

1. What are male motives for intercourse? Female? Why do you
        make love? How do those motives differ for males and fe-
        males? (love, physical pleasure)
2. What are the male, female erogenous zones? Do they differ?
3. What do males, females, find arousing? Do these differ?
4. What is attractive to you in a member of the opposite gender?
5. What makes males, females, feel vulnerable about sex?

Allow about 20 minutes for this part. It might be helpful for each group to select one person to serve as a recorder to make the report in Part 2. (It is possible that students will try to "cop out" in this phase by denying that there are any differences. Several strategies might be used to deal with this. One is to make them justify the assertion. Another is to challenge it with some obvious fact which documents a difference, e.g., orgasm rates, possibility of conception for the female.)

Part 2. Bring the groups back together. Have each group report its conclusions. Then have the other group react to their conclusions. For example, have the males tell the females in what ways they (the females) were wrong, and in what ways they were right about male sexuality.

Concepts that may need to be raised if overlooked by students:
1. Intragender variability may be greater than between-gender
        variability--need to consider the person as an individual
        rather than a typical male or a typical female.
2. Possibility of developmental changes--the gender differences
        in sexuality that are true in high school or college may
        have changed radically by middle age.

B. Perceived gender differences demonstration. This demonstration illustrates to students how we stereotype male and female sexuality and how we tend to overestimate gender differences.

Show the class a slide or picture that is erotic (such as a male and female together in states of semi-nudity). Each student should provide the following information on a sheet of paper:

1. How arousing I find this slide

   not at all   highly
   arousing   1   2   3   4   5   6   7   arousing

2. How arousing the average member of the opposite gender would find this slide

   not at all   highly
   arousing   1   2   3   4   5   6   7   arousing

3. Gender: male   female

Collect the data from students and compute the following 4 means:

males		females	
actual mean self-rating	mean rating attributed to them by females	actual mean self-rating	mean rating attributed to them by males

The standard results are:
  a. the actual mean self-ratings for males and females are fairly close (gender similarities), and
  b. females attribute very high levels of arousal to males, far more than males actually indicate, illustrating how we tend to stereotype.

VI. EVALUATION MATERIALS

Essay or research questions

1. How did Heiman study gender differences in arousal? How does her method differ from that used by Kinsey? Could the differences in their methods have any influence on the differences in their results? If so, why, and if not, why not? (See pp. 299-300 for Kinsey's and Heiman's data on arousal.)

2. Assume you are interested in studying the same kinds of questions as those researched by Shere Hite. What kinds of problems were there with her research and how would you go about attempting to eliminate those problems in your research design? (See pp. 308-310.)

3. Describe Kaplan's view of differences between male and female sexuality across the life span. Focussing on her description of gender differences in the approaches and feelings regarding sexuality during adolescence, indicate whether or not her analysis is in agreement with what you have observed among your friends of each

gender. How would you add to, or disagree with her views? (See pp. 307, 310-311 for Kaplan's views.)

4. What is Hyde's position regarding the notion that male impotence has been increased by female liberation? On what does she base her position? What is your position on the notion and on what do you base it? (See pp. 312-313 for Hyde's position.)

Multiple choice

1. Kinsey found that males had orgasms almost every time they had intercourse, whereas married females had orgasms about 75% of the time. Recent data on female orgasm indicate that this gender difference: a. has disappeared; b. has disappeared for all but about 5% of women; *c. remains, but women seem to be having orgasm with greater consistency; d. remains with about the same consistency of female orgasms as in Kinsey's time. (pp. 296-297)

2. Kinsey suggested that, in general, sex was desired more often by: a. husbands than wives early in marriage; b. husbands than wives throughout marriage; c. wives than husbands during their middle age; *d. both a & c. (p. 297)

3. When asked the reason for engaging in their first act of inter-course, a very uncommon (14%) reason given by males was: *a. love for the girl; b. "just wanted to;" c. didn't want to hurt girl's feelings; d. curiosity. (p. 298)

4. Gender differences in masturbation: a. were not measured by Kinsey; b. were striking at the time of Kinsey's study, but didn't exist in Hunt's study; *c. were pronounced in both Kinsey's and Hunt's studies; d. were not measured by Hunt. (p. 298)

5. In studies of arousal to erotic material: a. Kinsey found a far greater number of males than females reported arousal; b. Schmidt & Sigusch found little difference between males' and females' reported arousal; c. the data indicate little change since Kinsey's time; d. both a & c; *e. both a & b. (p. 299)

6. In her study of male vs. female arousal to various tapes, Heiman found that: a. explicit sex was most arousing for both; b. males rated erotic tapes as more arousing than females did; c. females rated erotic tapes as more arousing than males did; *d. both a & c; e. both a & b. (p. 300)

7. In Heiman's study of arousal: a. males found the female-initi-ated, female-centered tape most arousing; b. females found the

male-initiated, female-centered tape most arousing; c. females found the female-initiated, female-centered tape most arousing; *d. both a & c. (p. 300)

8. In Heiman's study: a. males were sometimes unaware of their own arousal; *b. females were sometimes unaware of their own arousal; c. females never made errors in self reports of their own arousal; d. neither gender made errors in self reports of arousal. (p. 300)

9. Heiman's study dealt only: *a. with the preliminary stages of arousal; b. with arousal in the context of hearing erotic tapes in the presence of subjects' usual sexual partner; c. with visual erotica; d. with responses to arousal by married persons. (p. 299)

10. According to research, which of the following is not a contemporary difference in male and female sexuality? a. males have more orgasms in marital intercourse than do females; *b. males are more aroused by erotic stimuli than are females; c. males can judge whether or not they're aroused better than females can; d. males and females reach their "peak" of sexual desire at different ages. (pp. 299-300)

11. The speculation that anatomy may explain sex differences in masturbation is, basically, that: a. male anatomy is most important for impregnation; b. female anatomy is most important for nurturance during pregnancy and childcare; *c. male sexual anatomy and arousal are more visible than that of females; d. both a & b. (pp. 302-303)

12. Importance was not attached to mutual orgasm in marriage manuals until the: a. 1900's; *b. 1930's; c. 1950's; d. 1970's. (pp. 302-303)

13. Our major source of information about the influence of hormones on sexuality comes: a. from Masters & Johnson; b. from Kinsey; c. from Hunt; *d. from animal studies. (p. 304)

14. Females have about ___ the level of testosterone that males have. a. 1/2; b. 1/4; *c. 1/6; d. male/female ratios of testosterone are unknown. (p. 304)

15. Hyde criticizes the notion of gender differences on differing levels of testosterone because: a. it may be that cells in the hypothalamus or genitals of women are more sensitive to testosterone than are these cells in men; b. the effects of testosterone on sexuality have not been studied; c. the effects of testosterone on human sexuality are not well documented; d. it ignores the increase in male sexuality produced by injections of estrogen; *e. both a & c. (p. 304)

16. The ___ of males and the ___ of females ___ premarital sex in
    ___'s study. a. majority, minority, engaged in, Kinsey;
    b. majority, majority, approved of, Hunt; c. majority, majority,
    engaged in, Hunt; *d. all of the above. (pp. 304-305)

17. Research in the 1970's indicated that ___% of sexually active
    girls used contraception occasionally or not at all. a. 25;
    b. 50; *c. 75; d. data are not available for this question.
    (p. 305)

18. The earliest sexual experiences for: a. both males and females
    is masturbation; b. males is with heterosexual petting and for
    females is with masturbation; *c. females is with heterosexual
    petting and for males is with masturbation; d. both males and
    females is with homosexual petting. (p. 307)

19. Much of the research on gender differences in sexuality has
    concentrated on: a. clinical patients; b. animals; *c. college
    students; d. married people. (p. 307)

20. Based on the notions of Kaplan & Reiss, Hyde suggests that:
    a. people begin in adolescence with body-centered sexuality,
    then later develop person-centered sexuality; b. people begin
    in adolescence with person-centered sexuality, then later develop
    body-centered sexuality; *c. males are characterized by "a", fe-
    males are characterized by "b"; d. males are characterized by
    "b", females are characterized by "a". (pp. 310-312)

21. In their study of male sexuality, Pietropinto & Simenauer found
    that the majority of men were irritated by a woman who: a. made
    the first advance; b. made sexual demands; c. seemed "too easy";
    *d. none of the above; fewer than 5% were irritated by any of
    these. (p. 311)

22. Jenny, concerned because John doesn't seem very excited by
    their sex life, has read the results of Pietropinto & Simen-
    auer's study. Based on the responses of the males in that
    study, Jenny probably decides to: a. behave in a more pas ve
    fashion to avoid threatening John; b. behave in a coy, indirect
    manner to try to get him to initiate sex; c. actively initiate
    sex with John; d. suggest mutual mouth-genital stimulation the
    next time they make love; *e. both c & d. (p. 311)

23. Hite's training includes: a. an M.D. degree; *b. an M.A. in
    history; c. a Ph.D. in clinical psychology; d. a B.A. in psy-
    chology. (p. 308)

24. Hite's research primarily involved: a. studying the relation-
    ship between testosterone and arousability in rats; b. hiding
    under the beds of male and female prostitutes; *c. distributing
    questionnaires to readers of feminist magazines; d. observing
    animal sexual behavior; e. both a & d. (p. 308)

136

25. Roughly ___ of Hite's subjects experienced orgasm during intercourse without separate massaging of the clitoris. *a. a quarter; b. a half; c. three-quarters; d. ninety percent. (p. 309)

26. The main value of Hite's study lies in its: a. excellent sampling technique; b. rigorous use of experimental methods; *c. first person accounts of female sexual experience; d. use of well trained interviewers. (pp. 309-310)

27. Data from Hunt's study suggest that a trend toward gender similarities will continue in the areas of: a. masturbation; b. premarital sex; c. extramarital sex; d. both a & b; *e. both b & c. (p. 312)

28. The hypothesis that the sexual liberation of women causes impotence in men has been: a. supported by experimental data collected by psychotherapists; b. supported by experimental data collected by sex therapists; c. supported by experimental data collected by sex researchers; *d. unexplored by experimental methods, therefore causation cannot be inferred. (p. 312)

29. The hypothesis that women have an innately stronger sex drive than men has been: supported by experimental data collected by sex researchers; b. advanced by Masters & Johnson; c. unstudied using experimental methods; *d. both b & c. (p. 313)

30. Compared to earlier studies, recent research suggests that males are: a. more likely to have problems experiencing coital orgasm; b. less likely to use prostitutes; c. less promiscuous; *d. all of the above. (p. 312)

True/False

1. Women, on the average, seem to have orgasms during coitus with less consistency than men do (T, pp. 296-297).

2. Kinsey believed that men's orgasm occurred so close to 100% of the time that they engaged in intercourse that he didn't bother to tabulate statistics on male orgasm consistency (T, pp. 296-297).

3. Comparisons of the Kinsey and Hunt studies would suggest no change in the gender differences in orgasm consistency (F, pp. 296-297).

4. According to the recent Redbook survey, 1/3 of the wives wished they had intercourse more often (T, p. 297).

5. Hunt's data indicate that almost all males and females have masturbated to orgasm at least once (F, p. 298).

6. Hyde speculates that comparisons of Kinsey's and Hunt's data on the percentage of females masturbating suggest that females did not feel free to report their masturbation during Kinsey's time (F, p. 298).

7. The percentages of males and females reporting that they had masturbated to orgasm at least once in Hunt's study are very close to those reported by Kinsey's subjects thirty years ago (T, p. 298).

8. In Kinsey's sample, although most men reported having been aroused by erotic stories, half the females had never seen an erotic story (F, p. 299).

9. In Schmidt & Sigusch's study of arousal to erotic material, women showed an increase in petting and coitus within the 24 hours after exposure to the material, whereas men did not (T, p. 299).

10. In Heiman's study on arousal to erotic material, women were generally aroused by the same material that men were (T, p. 300).

11. Differences in indications of female arousal from physiological vs. self-report measures in Heiman's study are most likely due to the females' embarrassment at admitting their arousal (F, p. 300).

12. In the 1800's, it was assumed that females did not experience sexual desire (T, p. 302).

13. The hormonal explanation of gender differences in sexuality is based on the finding that estrogen inhibits female sexual response (F, p. 304).

14. A double standard exists when the same sexual behavior is evaluated differently depending on whether a male or a female did it (T, p. 304).

15. A large majority of both young males and females in Hunt's sample engaged in premarital sex (T, pp. 304-305).

16. Females in Hunt's sample seemed to believe in a double standard more than males did regarding the acceptability of premarital sex (T, p. 304).

17. The average female needs at least 3 or 4 times longer than the average male to reach orgasm by masturbation (F, p. 306).

18. Kinsey found that women who masturbated before marriage were more likely to have orgasm during the first year of marriage (T, p. 306).

19. Women generally have orgasms more consistently at 40 than they did at age 25 (T, p. 307).

20. A slight majority of the women in Hite's sample regularly had orgasm during intercourse without separate massaging of the clitoris (F, p. 309).

21. Male sexuality is showing some tendency to change in the direction of female patterns of sexuality (T, p. 312).

Matching

Match these people with the work on male/female sexuality they have done.

____ 1. Hite

____ 2. Kaplan

____ 3. Heiman

____ 4. Schmidt & Sigusch

____ 5. Pietropinto & Simenauer

a. studied responses to erotic slides and movies and did a 24 hour follow-up on sexual behavior.

b. studied responses to erotic tapes and measured physiological responses as well as self-reported responses.

c. sex therapist who wrote an analysis of gender differences in sexuality across the life span.

d. collected questionnaire responses to a large number of American males regarding their sexual attitudes and behavior.

e. collected questionnaire responses to a large number of American females regarding their sexual attitudes and behavior.

Matching answer key: 1. e; 2. c; 3. b; 4. a; 5. d.

CHAPTER 14: HOMOSEXUALITY AND BISEXUALITY

I. LEARNING OBJECTIVES

Study of this chapter should enable the student to:

1. Know the meaning of the various terms associated with homosexual behavior and the people who engage in it.

2. Describe the attitudes and stereotypes about gays and indicate the extent to which research supports these stereotypes.

3. Indicate the various kinds of discrimination gays experience.

4. Describe the variations in gay life style including the baths, bars, tearoom trade, gay liberation, and gay publications.

5. Comment on the stereotype that gays are promiscuous and indicate what the research indicates for both males and females.

6. Define and distinguish between the following kinds of homosexuality: deprivation, latent, covert, and overt.

7. Describe Kinsey's method of determining the incidence of homosexual behavior in our society and indicate the extent to which homosexual behavior has increased in the past 30 years.

8. Describe and evaluate each of the research approaches used to determine whether or not those engaging in homosexual behavior are "sick". What is the position of the American Psychiatric Association?

9. Know what kinds of therapies have been employed with homosexuals. Are they appropriate?

10. Evaluate the different theoretical explanations of the causes of homosexuality, and based on the research, indicate your opinion of the cause.

11. Classify the individuals described in the Focuses in this chapter in terms of which variety of homosexuality they most closely resemble.

12. Compare and contrast homosexuality and bisexuality and indicate which makes more sense (or is most understandable) to you.

13. Describe the contributions to our understanding of homosexuality made by Freud, Kinsey, Bieber, Wolff, Kallman, Humphreys, Martin & Lyon, Weinberg & Williams, and Freedman.

II. CHAPTER AT A GLANCE

<u>Introduction</u> (pp. 316-317). Defines homosexual, gay, straight, ho-
mophile, and mentions various derogatory terms.

<u>Stereotypes and Discrimination</u> (pp. 317-321)
   <u>Attitudes Toward Homosexuality</u>: Majority disapproves.
   <u>Stereotypes About Gays</u>
      <u>The swish and the dyke</u>: Stereotype here represents a confu-
         sion between gender identity and choice of sexual partner.
      <u>The role-playing stereotype</u>: Majority don't restrict them-
         selves to dominant or submissive role.
      <u>The child-molester stereotype</u>: Only 20% of child-molesting
         is homosexual.
      <u>Jokes about gays</u>
   <u>Gays as a Minority Group</u>: Cites various instances of discrimina-
      tion.

<u>The Gay Lifestyle</u> (pp. 321-331)
   <u>Slang</u>
   <u>Varieties of Homosexuality</u>
      <u>Deprivation homosexuality</u>: Prisons, etc.
      <u>Latent homosexuality</u>: Discusses Freud's notions.
      <u>Covert and overt homosexuality</u>: Closet vs. open.
   <u>Varieties of Experience</u>
      <u>The bars</u>
      <u>The baths</u>
      <u>Promiscuity</u>: Cites Weinberg & Williams' study, notes that
         gay females tend less toward promiscuity than gay males.
      <u>The tearoom trade</u>: Notes Humphrey's book. Describes the
         practice.
      <u>Gay liberation</u>
      <u>Publications</u>: Notes existence of gay newspapers, magazines,
         and use of underground press' classified ads.

<u>Sexual Behavior</u> (p. 332): Defines terms used to describe aspects
   of homosexual intercourse.

<u>How Many People are Gay?</u> (pp. 332-334): Describes Kinsey's typol-
   ogy, and basically answers question on basis of that, since most
   other studies suggest similar conclusions.

<u>Homosexuality: Normal or Abnormal?</u> (pp. 334-337)
   <u>Sin and the Medical Model</u>
   <u>Research Results</u>
      <u>Clinical studies</u>: Notes sampling bias.
      <u>Studies with control groups</u>: Notes sampling bias.
      <u>Nonpatient research</u>: Describes works of Hooker, Freedman, and
         the changes in American Psychiatric Association's position.
   <u>Therapy for Homosexuality</u>: Briefly describes some approaches but
      notes that the whole concept of therapy conflicts with her con-
      clusion that homosexuality is not abnormal.

Why Do Some People Become Homosexual? (pp. 337-342)
  Biological Theories
    Hormonal imbalance: Notes no support in studies of males,
      some support from one as yet unreplicated study with fe-
      males.
    Prenatal hormone exposure: No direct evidence.
    Genetic factors: Describes Kallman's twin studies, notes that
      other researchers can't replicate Kallman.
  Psychoanalytic Theory
    Freudian theory
    Bieber's research: With males.
    Wolff's research: With females.
  Learning Theory
  Sociological Theory
  Empirical Data: No single factor has emerged and we don't know
    what causes homosexuality.

Bisexuality (pp. 342-345)

Summary (pp. 345-346)

Suggestions for Further Reading (p. 346)

Focuses:

  A Case History of Persecution: The boys of Boise (pp. 322-323)
  A gay couple: Tom and Brian (pp. 326-327)
  The ethics of sex research: The tearoom trade (p. 330)
  Case history of Joan: A bisexual woman (pp. 344-345)

III. GLOSSARY

  bisexual. A person who has some sexual contacts with males and
    some with females.

  butch. A very masculine lesbian; may also refer to a very mascu-
    line male homosexual.

  femme. A feminine lesbian.

  gay. Homosexual.

  heterosexual. A person who is sexually attracted to, or engages
    in sexual activity primarily with, members of the opposite
    gender.

  homosexual. A person who is sexually attracted to, or engages
    in sexual activity primarily with members of his or her own
    gender.

interfemoral intercourse. Sexual activity in which the penis moves between the thighs.

lesbian. A female homosexual.

IV. AUDIO-VISUAL AIDS

Movies:

In winterlight. Multi Media, 18 min., color, $220/$40. Shows two women as they share their lives and sexuality together, particularly hand-genital stimulation. The film is marred by the fact that both women are rather masculine looking, and one is particularly muscular, so that the film may reinforce stereotypes that lesbians are mannish.

Vir Amat. Multi Media, #550, 15 min., color, music only, $225/$35. Shows two gay young men who have lived together for over a year. After doing the dinner dishes together, they progress to sexual activity, including fellatio and mutual masturbation. There is some humorous and playful activity.

Holding. Multi Media, 15 min., color, $225/$35. Shows two young lesbians relating sexually, including mutual masturbation and cunnilingus. The film techniques are very artsy.

Homosexuality. CRM McGraw-Hill, 10 min., color, $195/$20. Shows two boys' reactions to thoughts that a friend is gay.

A woman's place is in the house. Texture, 30 min., color, $350/$45. Elaine Nobel, elected to the Massachusetts House of Representatives, discusses her gayness candidly.

V. DEMONSTRATIONS OR GROUP DISCUSSION

A. Gay speakers. Many campuses have a gay student union, which is happy to provide speakers to classes. This can simply be run as a question-and-answer session. It is a good learning experience for students, as they question their own attitudes about homosexuality and hear how gays feel.

B. Class project: Anti-gay humor. As a class project, assign each member of the class to watch a different hour or two of prime-time TV comedy or variety shows. Each student is to keep a count of the number of anti-gay jokes told in the hour, and the content of each. For comparison, they may also keep track of jokes about some other minority group, such as blacks. Students should bring their observations to the next class. From the data they have collected, they should discuss the following questions:

1. How common are anti-gay jokes? How common are they compared
     with jokes about some other minority group?
2. What kind of stereotypes or assumptions about gays are reflec-
     ted in the content of the jokes?
3. Do the available scientific data bear out the assumptions and
     stereotypes in #2 as being true or false?
4. If you were a gay person listening to those jokes, how would
     you feel?

   C. Role-play: Gays and their parents. The purpose of this exercise is to help students understand how gays feel when they "come
out" to someone, in particular their parents, and how parents feel
when they find they have a gay son or daughter.

   The characters are:
   John (Jennifer) - is a senior in college. About a year ago he
(she) did some serious thinking and decided he (she) definitely had
a homosexual identity. Since then he (she) has had a gay lover and
has been active in the gay organization on campus. He (she) has
finally decided to stop being dishonest with his (her) parents: he
(she) is home for Christmas vacation and is having a discussion with
them for the purpose of coming out to them.
   The two parents - are college-educated, middle class people. He
is a businessman, she teaches fifth grade. They have had no previous inkling about their son's (daughter's) homosexuality.

General instructions for role plays:

   1. Sometimes students are very threatened by role plays and are
reticent to participate in them. Having a demonstration role play
--perhaps by students from the theater department, or by the instructor and a student volunteer--may help to show the students what is
expected. It is also less threatening if there are several role
plays going on in the room simultaneously. Breaking the class into
groups of 6-8 students and having each group do the role play accom-
plishes this, and allows more students to participate actively. If
a number of role plays are done over the course of the term, students
become more comfortable with them.

   2. Students should be instructed to really try to be the character
they are playing, to get inside that person, to feel and say what
they would feel and say.

   3. The sequence of events in a role-playing session can be as
follows:
         a. Read the roles to the actors and allow them a minute or two
            to think about who they are to be.
         b. Proceed with the role plays for 10-15 min. (depending on how
            things go), with the others observing.
         c. After the role play, have each actor in turn discuss how she
            or he felt about being the person they played.

d. Have the observers tell what they thought and felt during the role play.

e. Have the group discuss how realistic they thought the role play was—would this situation have turned out this way if it were a true situation?

f. Have the group discuss what they learned from the role play.

D. Gay literature. The purpose of this is to familiarize students with current opinions in the gay community and to beome more familiar with the gay lifestyle.

The instructor brings copies of The Advocate, gay activist publications or gay pornography to the class and allows students to browse through them and discuss their contents.

VI. EVALUATION MATERIALS

Essay or research questions

1. Imagine that you're at a family gathering after you've completed reading this chapter, and, further that you've just discovered that your room mate in the dorm is gay, much to your amazement. You mention this to some of your family members and your brother-in-law says that you must be very naive, he would have been able to recognize a "queer". He launches into jokes and assertions about the three common stereotypes about gays. How would you respond (based on the research) to his beliefs? (See pp. 318-320.)

2. Describe the kind of relationship you would like to have with a present or potential partner in terms of your goals and ideals. How are your feelings similar or different from those expressed by Tom and Brian, the gay couple described in the Focus in Chapter 14? (See pp. 326-327.)

3. There have been three kinds of research designs used in the attempt to determine whether or not homosexuality is an illness. Describe each including their advantages and disadvantages from a methodological point of view and then describe the research design that you would use to study the issue. (See pp. 335-337.)

Multiple choice

1. Gay liberationists prefer the term "gay" to "homosexual" because "homosexual": a. emphasizes the sexual aspects of the lifestyles; b. can be used as a derogatory label; c. behavior is against the law in many states; d. all of the above; *e. both a & b. (p. 316)

2. Most Americans regard homosexuality as: a. "very obscene and
   vulgar"; b. harmful to American life; c. a curable ilness;
   *d. all of the above; e. both a & c. (p. 317)

3. The stereotype that gay males may be recognized by their "swish-
   iness" is: a. correct about half the time; *b. generally incorrect, as most gay males hold a masculine identity; c. generally
   correct, as most gay males wish they were female; d. a confusion
   between morality and gender identity. (p. 319)

4. The stereotype that gay females may be recognized by their masculine behavior is: *a. generally incorrect, as most gay females hold a feminine identity; b. correct about half the time;
   c. generally correct, as most gay females wish they were male;
   d. a confusion between morality and choice of sexual partner.
   (p. 319)

5. Role-playing among gay females appears to be: a. typical only
   during the sexual act itself; b. typical only outside the sex
   act (that is, one acts as housewife while the other earns money);
   c. typical both within and outside the sex act; *d. not typical
   either within or outside the sex act except among young women
   when they first enter the lesbian lifestyle. (p. 319)

6. ___% of child molesting is done by heterosexual men to little
   girls and ___% is homosexual. *a. 80, 20; b. 20, 80; c. 50, 50;
   d. 40, 60. (p. 320)

7. Fear of gays (as sometimes shown by derogatory jokes) is known
   as: a. homophilia; b. gayaterroria; *c. homophobia; d. none of
   the above; e. both a & b. (p. 320)

8. How do gays differ from other "minorities" such as blacks and
   women? a. job discrimination; b. tendency to engage in self-
   deprecating talk; *c. recognizability; d. all of the above.
   (pp. 320-321)

9. A "drag queen" is a homosexual: a. who cruises the bars in
   search of a partner; b. who is passive and waits for others to
   initiate a relationship; *c. male who dresses in women's clothing; d. who is not open about his/her choice of sexual partner;
   e. none of the above. (p. 323)

10. The concept of "latent" homosexuality was originated by:
    a. Martin & Lyon; *b. Freud; c. Hooker; d. Bieber; e. Wolff.
    (p. 324)

11. Freud suggested that some individuals who actively persecute gays
    in order to prove their own heterosexuality may be expressing:
    *a. reaction formation; b. repression; c. depression; d. perver-
    sion; e. regression. (p. 324)

12. In determining the kind of lifestyle a homosexual leads, it is
    important to know: a. whether the homosexuality is caused by
    biological or learned factors; b. whether the person is a covert
    or overt homosexual; c. whether the person is male or female;
    d. all of the above; *e. both b & c. (p. 325)

13. Weinberg & Williams found that the most common pattern was for a
    gay male to have ___ or more different sex partners in his life-
    time. a. 10; b. 50; c. 100; d. 500; *e. 1000. (p. 329)

14. Humphreys' research on the tearoom trade has been criticized
     for his: a. violation of the anonymity of his subjects;
     *b. failure to employ informed consent; c. use of shock in
     conducting therapy for gays; d. all of the above; e. both a &
     c. (p. 330)

15. Humphreys found that homosexuals in the tearoom trade typically
    use: a. interfemoral intercourse; *b. fellatio; c. anal inter-
    course; d. both a & c. (p. 331)

16. The homosexual act may be distinguished from the heterosexual
    act: *a. because both partners are of the same gender; b. be-
    cause of the kinds of techniques and positions used by gays;
    c. because heterosexuals do not engage in anal intercourse;
    d. all of the above; e. both a & b. (p. 332)

17. Kinsey's data on homosexuality indicates that: a. the percentage
    of people who are exclusively homosexual is small (2% or less);
    b. the percentage of people who have had some homosexual experi-
    ence is large (37% of males, 13% of females); c. the incidence
    of homosexuality among men is considerably higher than the inci-
    dence of homosexuality among women; *d. all of the above;
    e. both a & c. (pp. 332-333)

18. Over the past 30 years the percentage of people who are homosex-
    ual appears to be: a. increasing for males; b. increasing for
    females; c. increasing for females but stable for males;
    *d. fairly stable; e. none of the above. (p. 331)

19. Which of the following approaches to determining the relative
    sickness or health of homosexuals has the least problems methodo-
    logically? a. clinical studies; *b. nonpatient research;
    c. studies of homosexuals in therapy compared with control groups
    of heterosexuals in therapy; d. both a & c. (p. 335)

20. Hooker's research on homosexual adjustment involved asking clini-
    cians to identify which of each of 30 pairs of individuals was
    homosexual on the basis of their responses on the: a. Stanford-
    Binet; b. Thematic Apperception Test; *c. Rorschach; d. Draw-A-
    Person; e. all of the above. (p. 336)

21. The American Psychiatric Association classifies homosexuality as
    a: a. character disorder; b. personality disorder; c. neurosis;
    d. psychosis; *e. none of the above. (p. 337)

22. Hyde argues that therapy to stop homosexual behavior should be
    given to homosexuals: a. who are poorly adjusted as it is prob-
    ably the homosexuality that is causing it; *b. who request it
    because they say that the homosexual behavior is causing emo-
    tional distress; c. both of the above; d. none of the above;
    Hyde argues that persons should never receive therapy to stop
    their homosexual behavior since homosexuality is not an illness.
    (p. 337)

23. Which of these doesn't belong with the others? *a. negative
    Oedipus complex; b. hormonal imbalance; c. genetic factors;
    d. prenatal hormone exposure. (pp. 337-339)

24. The word "it" in "It won't make you heterosexual, it will only
    make you horny" refers to: *a. testosterone therapy; b. a
    voluptuous nude body; c. estrogen therapy; d. shock plus pic-
    tures of nude males. (p. 338)

25. The only study to provide any support for the hormonal imbalance
    explanation of homosexuality found higher: a. testosterone
    levels in homosexual than in heterosexual males; b. testosterone
    levels in heterosexual than in homosexual males; c. testosterone
    levels in homosexual than in heterosexual females; d. estrogen
    levels in heterosexual than in homosexual females; *e. both c &
    d. (pp. 337-338)

26. Kallman's study which found perfect concordance for homosexuality
    among all the identical twin pairs he studied doesn't provide
    strong support for the genetic explanation of homosexuality,
    since: a. there was also high concordance among the nonidenti-
    cal twin pairs when they were reared together; b. the identical
    twin pairs were reared together; c. other investigators have not
    been able to replicate Kallman's findings; d. all of the above;
    *e. both b & c. (p. 338)

27. With regard to the three biological explanations of homosexuality,
    there is: a. more support for the genetic hypothesis than for
    the other two; b. more support for the hormonal imbalance hypo-
    thesis than for the other two; c. more support for the prenatal
    hormone exposure hypothesis than for the other two; d. less sup-
    port for the genetic hypothesis than for the other two; *e. little
    evidence supporting any of the biological explanations. (p. 339)

28. Polymorphous perverse refers to: *a. the idea that the infant's
    sexuality is totally undifferentiated, and thus is directed
    toward all sorts of objects, both appropriate and inappropriate;
    b. the hypothesis that humans are innately bisexual; c. the

legal phrase used to accuse individuals of homosexuality in many states; d. the variety of different sexual acts in which homosexuals engage. (p. 339)

29. ___ held the belief that homosexuals are narcissistic, and that homosexuality represents making love to oneself. a. Freedman; *b. Freud; c. Weinberg & Williams; d. Kinsey; e. Kallman. (p. 339)

30. When all the studies aimed at determining the factors associated with homosexuality are examined, the one factor which emerges consistently is: a. distant or absent parent of other gender; b. cold, rejecting parent of other gender; c. weak, passive parent of same gender; d. dominant, authoritarian parent of other gender; *e. none of the above. (p. 343)

True/False

1. The word homosexual is derived from the Latin word "homo" meaning "man" (F, p. 316).

2. A large majority of Americans are against legalizing private homosexual behavior between adults (T, p. 317).

3. A small (11%) percentage of gays believe that homosexuality is an illness (T, p. 318).

4. The belief that male gays are feminine and that female gays are masculine represents a confusion of gender identity with choice of sexual partner (T, p. 319).

5. When two gay males live together, typically, one takes the submissive "wife" role while the other takes the dominant "husband" role (F, p. 319).

6. Research indicates that approximately a fifth of gay males show a preference for a particular role, with most gays often switching roles during the sex act (T, p. 319).

7. Role-playing (dominance, submissiveness, etc.) may be observed among young females when they first enter the lesbian lifestyle, but they tend to be discarded quickly because of the problems inherent in such roles (T, p. 319).

8. According to Hyde, the rejection of male-female role playing by many gay women is partially due to the fact that they are feminists (T, pp. 319-320).

9. Most adolescents are initiated into homosexuality by adult males (F, p. 320).

10. Kinsey reported that compared to heterosexual women, homosexual women have greater orgasm consistency (T, p. 321).

11. A "butch" refers either to a masculine gay male or masculine gay female (T, p. 324).

12. The overt homosexual passes for a heterosexual at work and in most social relationships (F, p. 324).

13. The covert homosexual makes no attempt to hide his or her homosexuality and may even be obvious about it (F, pp. 324-325).

14. Research indicates that heterosexuals who are victims of prison rape tend to become homosexual after leaving prison (F, p. 324).

15. There is a great deal of similarity between the lifestyles of gay males and gay females (F, p. 325).

16. Gay females suffer more discrimination than gay males (F, p. 325)

17. Research has found that gays tend to be considerably more creative than straights (F, p. 325).

18. Most gay bars are either for gay males or gay females rather than gender-integrated (T, p. 326).

19. Gay baths are almost exclusively for male homosexuals (T, p. 328)

20. Lesbians tend to be far less promiscuous than gay males (T, p. 329).

21. Many of the men who engaged in the tearoom trade in Humphreys' study were heterosexually married men (T, p. 331).

22. Some gays advertise for partners in underground newspapers like The Berkeley Barb because there are not, as yet, any gay newspapers or magazines (F, p. 331).

23. Before this century in Europe and the United States, the dominant belief was that homosexuality was an illness (F, p. 334).

24. A major breakthrough in research on homosexuality came with the use of clinical studies involving case histories (F, p. 335).

25. The general results from the nonpatient research studies indicate that nonpatient homosexuals do not differ from nonpatient heterosexuals in their adjustment (T, pp. 335-336).

26. Hooker's study found that even skilled clinicians can't tell heterosexuals from homosexuals on the basis of their responses to a projective personality measure (T, p. 336).

27. In 1973, the American Psychiatric Association voted to remove homosexuality from its list of disorders in the Diagnostic and Statistical Manual of Mental Disorders (T, p. 337).

28. Lesbians tend to have larger clitorises than heterosexual women (F, p. 338).

29. A child loves his father and identifies with his mother. This is known as the negative Oedipus complex (T, p. 339).

30. Bisexuality is far less common than exclusive homosexuality (F, p. 343).

Matching

Match the explanations of homosexuality with the appropriate theory.

____ 1. Identification with the parent of the other gender during childhood.

____ 2. Acceptance of role via self-fulfilling prophecy after label "homosexual" has been applied to the person.

____ 3. Found sexual relations with same gender reward-ing.

____ 4. Fears heterosexual rela-tions because parent of other gender was seductive and overly possessive.

____ 5. Punished for engaging in heterosexual behavior during adolescence.

a. Psychoanalytic theory

b. Learning theory

c. Sociological theory

1.a.   2.c.   3.b.   4.a.   5.b.

<u>Matching</u>

Match the researcher with the research.

___ 1. Presented data supporting
his argument that homosexuals are more mentally
healthy than heterosexuals.

___ 2. British psychiatrist who
compared nonpatient lesbians with nonpatient heterosexual women.

___ 3. Conducted psychoanalytic
comparison of male heterosexuals and male homosex-
uals; coined the term
"homoseductive mother".

___ 4. Studied homosexual behavior
in public bathrooms.

___ 5. Found that homosexual males
tend to have many more
partners in their lifetime
than heterosexual males in
probably the largest and
most thorough study of male
homosexuals.

a. Laud Humphreys

b. Irving Bieber

c. Mark Freedman

d. Charlotte Wolff

e. Weinberg & Williams

1.c. 2.d. 3.b. 4.a. 5.e.

CHAPTER 15: VARIATIONS IN SEXUAL BEHAVIOR

I. LEARNING OBJECTIVES

Study of this chapter should enable the student to:

1. Distinguish between the various definitions of sexual abnormality.

2. Discuss different kinds of fetishes from the standpoint of the normal-abnormal continuum, and understand how individuals may learn to become fetishists.

3. Describe the procedures involved in the sex-change operation from the time an individual decides he/she wants gender reassignment.

4. Understand and evaluate the attempts to explain transsexualism.

5. Discuss the implications of transsexualism from legal, religious, ethical, and psychological standpoints.

6. Give possible reasons for the differing ratios of men to women who request gender reassignment.

7. Define and indicate the frequency in the population of such behaviors as transvestism, sadism, masochism, voyeurism, exhibitionism, pedophilia, necrophilia, incest, bestiality, nymphomania, satyriasis, celibacy, troilism, saliromania, coprophilia, and urophilia.

8. Indicate what is known about the effects on children of incest and pedophilia.

9. Describe the kinds of male and female prostitutes, their psychological functioning and motivation, and the course of their careers.

10. Indicate the kind of men who use prostitutes, what percentages of men do so, and their reasons for visiting prostitutes.

11. Describe the roles of pimps and madams in prostitution.

II. CHAPTER AT A GLANCE

Introduction (p. 348)

When is Sexual Behavior Abnormal? (pp. 348-350)
 Definitions and Criteria: Includes those by Marmor, the American
  Psychiatric Association, plus statistical, sociological, and
  psychological approaches.
 Categories of Sexual Deviance: Includes Freud's, cross-cultural
  comparisons, and sociological (Gagnon & Simon) schemes.

Fetishism (pp. 350-352): Distinguishes between fetishes for body
 parts and those for inanimate objects.
 Media Fetishes: Leather, rubber, fur, silk, etc.
 Form Fetishes: Shoes, boots, lingerie, etc.
 The Normal-Abnormal Continuum
 Why Do People Become Fetishists? Brief learning theory explana-
  tion.

Transsexualism (pp. 352-358): Definition, ratios of males to females
 requesting gender reassignment, discussion of gender identity
 component, brief history of transsexualism.
 The Sex-Change Operation: Johns Hopkins procedure including evaluation and counseling, hormone therapy, living as member of
  new gender, and surgical procedures. Discusses relatively
  greater difficulties of female-to-male operation, and record
  of good post-operative adjustment for transsexuals.
 What Causes Transsexualism? Reviews the prenatal hormone exposure, pre-operative hormone level, and learning explanations.
  Discusses possible reasons for disproportionately high ratio
  of males to females requesting reassignment.
 Other Issues: Legal, psychological, ethical, and religious questions raised by transsexualism, issue of sexual preference,
  and discussion of Renee Richards' case and methods of gender
  determination.

Transvestism (pp. 358-360): Definition, descriptions of variations
 on the theme, and brief description of aversion therapy.

Sadism and Masochism (pp. 360-361): Definition, incidence in population, history of terms, and possible causes.

Voyeurism (pp. 361-362): Definition, behavioral descriptions.

Exhibitionism (pp. 362-363): Definition, incidence in population,
 proportion of those attempting rape.

Pedophilia (pp. 363-364): Definition, incidence in population, characterization of child molesters, effect on children.

Necrophilia (p. 364): Defined, diagnosed as extremely abnormal.

Incest (pp. 364-366): Definition, under-reporting of incest, forms, characterization of those committing incest, effects on children, genetic and social consequences.

Bestiality (p. 366): Definition, incidence.

Nymphomania and Satyriasis (pp. 366-367): Definition, discussion of gender role implications of use of terms.

Celibacy (p. 367): Definition, religious and other reasons for choice to be celibate, effect on health.

Prostitution (pp. 367-373): Definition.
Kinds of Prostitutes: Call girls, brothel and massage parlor employees, street walkers, bar girls, and baby pros.
Psychological Functioning of Prostitutes: 3 rationalizing strategies, motives for that career choice.
Pimps and Madams: Definition and role in prostitution.
The Career of a Prostitute: Including entry and reasons for it, apprenticeship, and leaving the life and reasons.
Customers: Demographic descriptions, reasons for use, declining incidence of men using prostitutes (Kinsey, Hunt statistics).
Male Prostitutes: Description of gigolos, hustlers.

Miscellany (pp. 373-374): Rare variations including troilism, saliromania, coprophilia, and urophilia.

Summary (p. 374)

Suggestions for Further Reading (p. 374)

Focuses:

III. GLOSSARY

bestiality. Sexual contact with an animal; also called zoophilia.

celibate. Unmarried; also used to refer to someone who abstains from sexual activity.

corprophilia. A sexual variation in which arousal is associated with defecation or feces.

exhibitionist. A man who derives sexual gratification from exposing his genitals to others.

fetishism. A sexual variation in which an inanimate object causes sexual arousal.

gigolo. A male who sells his sexual services to women.

incest. Sexual intercourse between close relatives, such as a brother and sister.

masochism. A sexual variation in which the person derives sexual pleasure from experiencing physical or mental pain.

necrophilia. A sexual variation in which there is attraction to a corpse.

nymphomania. An extraordinarily high, insatiable sex drive in a woman.

pander. To procure a prostitute for a client; sometimes used to mean any catering to another's sexual desires.

paraphilia. A sexual variation.

pederasty. Sexual relations between a man and a boy; sometimes also used to mean anal intercourse.

pedophilia. A sexual variation in which an adult is sexually attracted to children; child molesting.

perversion. A sexual deviation.

pimp. One who procures a prostitute's services for another; a prostitute's protector.

prostitution. Indiscriminate sexual activity for payment.

sadism. A sexual variation in which the person derives sexual pleasure from inflicting pain on someone else.

satyriasis. An extraordinarily high level of sex drive in a male.

transsexual. A person who feels that he or she is trapped in the body of the wrong gender; a person who undergoes a sex-change operation.

transvestism. Dressing in the clothing of the opposite gender.

troilism. A sexual variation in which three people engage in sexual activity together.

urophilia (or urolagnia). A sexual variation in which the person derives sexual pleasure from urine or urination.

voyeurism. A sexual variation in which the person derives sexual pleasure from watching nudes or watching others have sexual intercourse; also called scoptophilia and Peeping Tomism.

IV. AUDIO-VISUAL AIDS

Movies:

Sex and gender. Multi Media, #445, 20 min., B & W, $240/$50.
Explores attitudes about gender identity through candid interviews with transsexuals and transvestites intercut with sequences of professional female impersonators backstage. Dr.
Virginia (Charles) Prince adds comments on transvestite and
transsexual phenomena.

Hookers. Multi Media, #220, 25 min., $330/$50. Filmed in colla-
boration with Margo St. James and COYOTE, this is a controver-
sial showing of a "working woman's" point of view. Interviews
with several women are interspersed with episodes of their
meetings with clients.

Radical sex styles. Grove Press, 50 min., B & W, $500/$60. Provides six candid interviews with people willing to discuss
frankly their private lives. Includes a beautiful transvestite who passes easily as a young woman, a man and two women
who have lived together for three years as a menage-a-trois,
a nymphomaniac, a bright, perceptive lesbian who discusses the
problems and pleasures of the gay life, an articulate bisexual who reveals a variety of sado-masochistic practices,
and a young married couple who perform in pornographic films
and live sex shows and participate in organized group sex.

V. DEMONSTRATIONS OR GROUP DISCUSSION

Guest speakers. A transsexual or prostitute can provide one of
the most interesting and educational experiences for students. A
question and answer discussion format may be helpful for the speaker
with the instructor soliciting written questions during the class
session preceding the speaker's appearance. A local mental health
center or the police may be able to put you in touch with a speaker.
The Erickson Educational Foundation, 1627 Moreland Ave., Baton Rouge,
La. 70808 keeps a registry of transsexuals in this country, and may
be able to help you find a speaker.

VI. EVALUATION MATERIALS

Essay or research questions

1. Our gender role expectations appear to interact with several aspects of our notions about normal and abnormal sexual variations. Describe several sexual variations for which these expectations may be important. (See pp. 352-354, 358-360, 362, 366-367 for material on transsexualism, exhibitionism and transvestism. Students might like to do research on the effect of stereotyping by writing several stories relating a situation in which the subject of the story desires very high levels of sexual activity. The story should remain constant with the exception of changing the name of the subject (Jim vs. Jill), and then students might ask other students around campus to indicate on a 7-point scale (7 - very likely, 1 - very unlikely) the extent to which they think the subject is a nymphomaniac or satyr. Mean scores should be higher for Jill than Jim.)

2. You have wished all your life that you had been born as a member of the opposite gender. You've been to see a number of doctors to try to find out why, and finally you decide to seek gender reassignment through sex change surgery. Describe (a) current hypotheses for the cause of transsexualism, (b) the extent to which these hypotheses have been supported by research, and (c) the steps generally required before the sex-change operation is performed. (See pp. 354-357.)

Multiple choice

1. "Sexual behavior that is done by very few people is deviant." This represents: *a. a statistical definition; b. the sociological approach; c. the American Psychiatric Association's definition; d. a psychological definition. (p. 349)

2. Hyde defines sexual behavior as deviant or abnormal when it is uncomfortable for the person, inefficient, bizarre, and/or causes physical or psychological harm to oneself or others. This definition borrows heavily from: a. the statistical definition; b. the sociological approach; c. the American Psychiatric Association's definition; *d. the psychological definition. (p. 349)

3. In categorizing sexual variations, a distinction between variations of sexual aim and variations of sexual object was proposed by: *a. Freud; b. Marmor; c. Gagnon & Simon; d. Hyde. (pp. 349-350)

4. According to Freud, bestiality is a variation in sexual: a. aim; *b. object; c. drive; d. curiosity. (p. 350)

5. According to Freud, ___ is a variation in sexual aim. *a. exhibitionism; b. incest; c. fetishism; d. pedophilia. (p. 350)

6. Homosexuality and prostitution are examples of Gagnon & Simon's ___ deviance. a. normal; b. pathological; *c. community producing; d. individual. (p. 350)

7. The case history of a shoe fetishist illustrates a ___ fetish. a. media; *b. form; c. biologically produced; d. incurable. (pp. 351-353)

8. ___ is within the range of normal sexual behavior. a. The desire to have your partner wear black silk lingerie; b. Masturbating with your partner's black silk panties; c. Inability to become aroused unless your partner wears silk panties; *d. both a & b; e. All of the above. (p. 351)

9. The female-to-male transsexual: a. is less common than the male-to-female transsexual; b. sex change surgery is more difficult than that for the male-to-female transsexual; *c. both of the above; d. none of the above. (pp. 352-353)

10. The effect of estrogen therapy for the transsexual is to: a. increase fat deposits producing rounded hips and enlarged breasts; b. decrease balding; c. decrease the frequency of erections; d. both a & c; *e. all of the above. (pp. 354-355)

11. Androgen therapy for the transsexual produces all but one of the following. Which does **not** happen? a. A beard may develop; b. The voice deepens; c. The clitoris enlarges; *d. Breasts disappear. (pp. 354-355)

12. Which of these hypotheses regarding the causes of transsexualism has received the most support from research? a. prenatal exposure to hormones of the other gender; b. abnormally high levels of hormones of the other gender before gender reassignment; *c. learning inappropriate gender role from parental socialization; d. both a & b. (p. 356)

13. When the buccal smear test is given, a Barr body should be present: *a. if the sex chromosomes are XX; b. if the sex chromosomes are XY; c. if the sex chromosomes are YY; d. if the sex chromosomes are XYY. (p. 357)

14. Which of the following is **not** true about transvestism? a. One authority estimates that more than a million people are involved in it in our country; b. The vast majority of transvestites are heterosexual; *c. Slightly more than half of the transvestites are male; d. It is a generally harmless, victimless sexual variation. (p. 359)

15. Potentially dangerous voyeurs can be identified as those who:
a. enter a building in order to view their victim; b. draw the attention of their victim to the fact that they are watching; c. masturbate while they are watching; *d. both a & b; e. all of the above. (p. 362)

16. The most common kind of exhibitionist: *a. is the repetitive, compulsive offender; b. is a mental deficient; c. is a drunk; d. has attempted or seriously contemplated rape. (p. 362)

17. Surveys have shown that approximately ___ of children have been approached by child molestors. a. 5-15%; *b. 20-40%; c. 45-65%; d. 70-85%. (p. 363)

18. Which of the following is not true of child molesters? a. They are acquainted with the children in the majority of cases; *b. They use force in just under half the cases; c. Molestation is usually limited to genital fondling; d. Some of the contacts are initiated by the child; e. They tend to be from the lower class. (p. 363)

19. The effect of being molested appears to be psychologically damaging to the child: a. almost always; b. when violence or extreme coercion is used; c. when the sexual contacts are serious and repeated a number of times; d. all of the above; *e. both b & c. (p. 364)

20. All but one of the following may be quite normal in mild forms. Which is not? a. fetishism; b. sadism; c. masochism; *d. necrophilia; e. both b & c. (p. 364)

21. Contrary to popular opinion, authorities believe that ___ contact is the most common form of incest. a. father-daughter; b. father-son; c. mother-son; *d. brother-sister. (p. 364)

22. The most prestigious of prostitutes is the: a. baby pro; b. massage parlor employee; *c. call girl; d. street walker; e. brothel employee. (p. 369)

23. Mary is a call girl. She's from a lower-class background, heterosexual in her private life and has high "business" expenses. She differs from most call girls with respect to her: *a. background; b. sexual preference; c. high business expenses; d. both b & c; e. all of the above. (p. 370)

24. The majority of prostitutes are: a. baby pros; b. massage parlor employees; c. call girls; *d. street walkers; e. brothel employees. (p. 370)

25. The case history of the shoe fetishist was from the files of: a. Freud; b. Ellis; *c. Krafft-Ebing; d. Masters & Johnson. (p. 352)

26. The case history of the shoe fetishist in the text would support
    the hypothesis that his fetish was caused by: *a. a learned
    association; b. a biological abnormality; c. sadistic tendencies;
    d. an overly active Id; e. his job as a shoe salesman. (p. 352)

27. The case history of nymphomania in the text mainly illustrates
    that: a. gender role expectations sometimes cause the label to
    be inappropriately applied; b. biological factors are sometimes
    responsible for this affliction; *c. the disorder involves com-
    pulsive and unsatiated intercourse; d. this is the reason for
    entry into prostitution in many cases. (p. 367)

True/False

1. Sexual behavior varies a great deal from culture to culture (T,
    p. 348).

2. According to Hyde, there are three major forms of fetishes inclu-
    ding fixation on body parts, inanimate objects, and particular
    animals (F, p. 350).

3. In the form fetish, it is the material out of which an object is
    made that is important to its erotic value (F, pp. 350-351).

4. More males than females request gender reassignment (T, pp. 352-
    353).

5. Transsexualism is a relatively modern phenomenon, found only in
    industrialized countries (F, p. 354).

6. Hormone therapy is given to the transsexual beginning at about
    6 months before surgery and continuing until approximately one
    year after surgery (F, pp. 354-355).

7. For about 6 months following surgery, the transsexual's vagina
    must be dilated with a plastic device so that it doesn't reclose
    (T, p. 355).

8. Under the administration of hormones, the transsexual's penis
    gradually develops erectile capacity (F, p. 355).

9. Research on the adjustment of transsexuals following gender re-
    assignment has indicated that they are generally very happy in
    their new gender (T, pp. 355-356).

10. No direct evidence has been found to support the hypothesis that
    transsexualism is caused by receiving prenatal hormones of the
    wrong gender (T, p. 356).

11. Studies of the hormone levels of transsexuals before gender reassignment have found abnormally high levels of hormones characteristic of the gender they wish to be (F, p. 356).

12. The true transvestite gets sexual gratification from cross-dressing, thus transvestism is probably basically a fetish (T, p. 358).

13. The vast majority of transvestites are homosexual (F, p. 359).

14. Transvestism is essentially unknown among women (T, p. 359).

15. There are more sadists than masochists (F, p. 360).

16. A masochist would find it arousing if he/she slammed his/her finger in a door (F, pp. 360-361).

17. Sadomasochism is a rare form of sexual behavior (T, p. 361).

18. Most voyeurs function well heterosexually (F, p. 362).

19. Exhibitionism accounts for roughly one-third of all arrests for sexual offenses (T, p. 362).

20. About 10% of exhibitionists have attempted or seriously contemplated rape (T, p. 362).

21. The child molester rarely uses force or attempts intercourse (T, p. 363).

22. Most child molesters are from the middle class (F, p. 364).

23. Research on incest has been done almost exclusively on people arrested and/or convicted for the offense (T, p. 364).

24. Most incidents of bestiality occur among single adult male farm workers (F, p. 366).

25. There is no evidence that celibacy is damaging to one's health (T, p. 367).

26. About half of all prostitutes are lesbians (F, p. 370).

27. Approximately 25% of prostitutes were actually forced into the profession (F, p. 371).

28. The use of prostitutes by middle-class males has been decreasing over the past 30 years (T, p. 372).

29. Hustlers are women who solicit men in bars (F, p. 373).

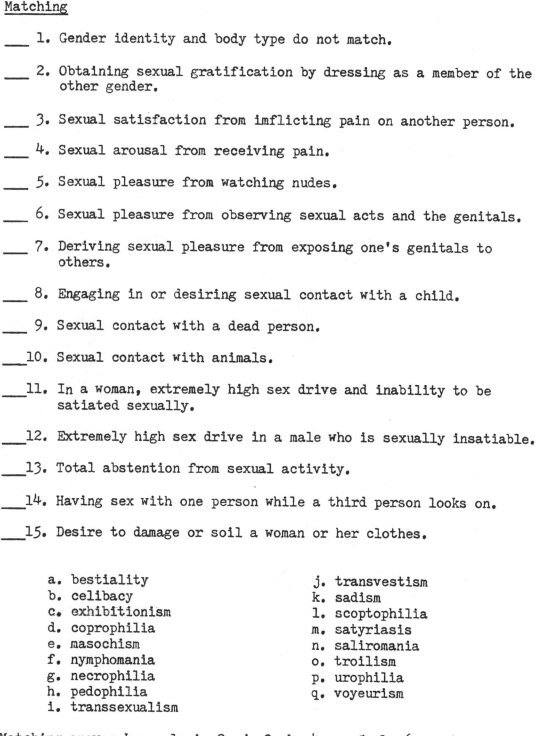

Matching

____ 1. Gender identity and body type do not match.

____ 2. Obtaining sexual gratification by dressing as a member of the other gender.

____ 3. Sexual satisfaction from imflicting pain on another person.

____ 4. Sexual arousal from receiving pain.

____ 5. Sexual pleasure from watching nudes.

____ 6. Sexual pleasure from observing sexual acts and the genitals.

____ 7. Deriving sexual pleasure from exposing one's genitals to others.

____ 8. Engaging in or desiring sexual contact with a child.

____ 9. Sexual contact with a dead person.

____10. Sexual contact with animals.

____11. In a woman, extremely high sex drive and inability to be satiated sexually.

____12. Extremely high sex drive in a male who is sexually insatiable.

____13. Total abstention from sexual activity.

____14. Having sex with one person while a third person looks on.

____15. Desire to damage or soil a woman or her clothes.

a. bestiality
b. celibacy
c. exhibitionism
d. coprophilia
e. masochism
f. nymphomania
g. necrophilia
h. pedophilia
i. transsexualism

j. transvestism
k. sadism
l. scoptophilia
m. satyriasis
n. saliromania
o. troilism
p. urophilia
q. voyeurism

Matching answer key: 1. i; 2. j; 3. k; 4. e; 5. l; 6. q; 7. c;
  8. h; 9. g; 10. a; 11. f; 12. m; 13. b; 14. 0; 15. n.

CHAPTER 16: RAPE

I. LEARNING OBJECTIVES

Study of this chapter should enable the student to:

1. Understand some of the effects of rape on the victims.

2. Describe the work being done by Burgess & Holmstrom on the rape trauma syndrome.

3. Differentiate between the acute phase and the long term reorganization phase for the victim, and describe the silent rape reaction.

4. Indicate the ways in which female socialization may contribute to women's vulnerability to rape.

5. Know the extent to which there are similarities among rapists.

6. Describe Cohen's typology of rapists, indicate the best strategy for dealing with each and specify why the strategy may be effective.

7. Understand what is meant by the date rape and describe the research on it.

8. Indicate ways in which males are socialized which may contribute to the likelihood that they will commit rape.

9. Differentiate between the psychopathological and socialization explanations of rape.

10. Describe the potential effect of fear of rape on women's feelings and behavior as well as on men (as in the prison situation).

11. Indicate possible ways of (a) dealing with rapists, and (b) changing socialization patterns to reduce the likelihood that rape will occur.

II. CHAPTER AT A GLANCE

Introduction (p. 376)

The Rape Victim (pp. 376-382)
Psychological Responses of the Rape Victim: Describes Burgess & Holmstrom's work at Boston City Hospital with the rape trauma syndrome and its acute phase and long term reorganization phase.
Silent Rape Reaction
Female Socialization: Creating Rape Victims: Notes that such stereotypically feminine traits as weakness, nurturance, altruism, and "ladylike" behavior increase female vulnerability to rape.

Rapists (pp. 382-388)
The Typical Rapist: Lists the few generalizations that can be made.
A Typology of Rapists: Presents Cohen's typology of four variations based on the motivation (sex, aggression) of the rapist.
The Date Rape: Describes Kanin's research.
Male Socialization: Creating Rapists: Notes that there are two theoretical views about the cause of rape: psychopathology view and the male role socialization view and lists traits associated with the male role which may contribute.
Prison Rape: Presents case history.

The Wider Impact of Rape (p. 388): Describes the potential effect of fear of rape on women's freedom and on their relations with men.

Preventing Rape (pp. 388-390): Discussion of self-defense and its limitations, but suggests that changes in male and female socialization are needed.

Summary (pp. 390-391)

Focuses:

The Story of a Rape Victim: Denise (pp. 378-379)
Case History of a Rapist: Phillip (pp. 384-385)

III. GLOSSARY

rape. Forcible sexual relations with an individual without that person's consent.

statutory rape. Sexual relations with a person who is below the legal "age of consent."

IV. AUDIO-VISUAL AIDS

Although there are a few films available, we have not yet seen any of them and do not have addresses for them. If you have a local rape crisis center, you may want to ask them if they have any audio-visual material that you could borrow.

V. DEMONSTRATIONS OR GROUP DISCUSSION

Guest speaker: <u>Rape Crisis Center</u>. Many campuses now have a rape crisis center. Ask one of the workers at the center to come to the class to explain the services offered by the center, and describe some of the experiences of the women who have come to the center for help.

Guest speaker: <u>self defense</u>. Ask a karate instructor or other self-defense expert, or someone from the police department, to speak to the class on simple methods of self defense from rapists.

VI. EVALUATION MATERIALS

Essay or research questions

1. Describe Kanin's research on date rape including his method and findings. Indicate the extent to which you or a friend of yours have had experiences which parallel his findings and suggest changes in the behavior of <u>both</u> the man and the woman on the date which would have reduced the likelihood of sexual assault. (See pp. 381-382, 385-387.)

2. Having read the chapter on rape, how would you go about raising your potential children - both male and female - to reduce the probability of creating a rapist or rape victim? (See pp. 381-382, 386-387, 388-390.)

3. Your cousin has taken a waitress job in a large city and is worried about the fact that she will be arriving home at about 2 a.m. after work, and asks you for advice. Although you have advised her to enroll in a self-defense course, describe at least five ways she could resist a potential rapist if she gets attacked. (See pp. 389-390.)

Multiple choice

1. About ___ of rapes go unreported. *a. 80%; b. 60%; c. 40%; d. 20%; e. 5%. (p. 376)

2. When intercourse takes place with a girl below the age of consent, it is known as ___ rape. a. pedophiliac; *b. statutory; c. molestation; d. non-consent; e. none of the above. (p. 376)

3. In most states, the legal age of consent for intercourse ranges
   from: a. 7-15; b. 10-14; *c. 12-16; d. 16-18; e. 18-21.
   (p. 376)

4. The rape trauma syndrome refers to: a. the conditions in a
   male's socialization which predisposes him to become a rapist;
   b. the conditions existing in the male's emotional life immedi-
   ately preceding his decision to attempt rape; c. the physical
   effects of rape on a woman's body; *d. the emotional changes
   that a woman undergoes following attempted or actual rape.
   (p. 377)

5. In the ___ phase of the rape trauma syndrome, ___ are especially
   prominant. *a. acute, fear and self-blame; b. acute, anger and
   anxiety; c. long term reorganization, fear and self-blame;
   d. long term reorganization, anger and anxiety. (p. 377)

6. Which of the questions of a rape victim is no longer permitted
   under the "reform" evidence laws? a. Have you ever had intercourse with the alleged rapist; b. Did you give your consent to
   the act; *c. Were you a virgin, prior to the rape; d. How did
   the defendant (rapist) force you. (p. 380)

7. Judges see some rapes as being "consensual intercourse" which
   they describe as: a. friendly rape; b. felonious gallantry;
   c. assault with failure to please; *d. all of the above; e. none
   of the above.

8. The "silent rape reaction" is: a. fear on the part of the victim
   to scream or otherwise call for help while she is being raped;
   b. failure to report the rape to police; c. failure to tell any
   friends or family members about the rape; d. a period of scream-
   ing hysteria after which the victim lapses into utter silence
   for a period of several weeks; *e. both b & c. (p. 380)

9. Most rapists are: *a. under 25; b. unmarried; c. unemployed;
   d. atheists. (p. 382)

10. It is estimated that the rapist tends to murder his victim:
    a. only when she resists as it makes him angry; b. only when
    she doesn't resist as his excitement comes from her resistance;
    *c. very rarely (about 1 murder per 500 rapes); d. both b & c;
    e. both a & c. (pp. 382-383)

11. This type of rapist is the most dangerous although he uses no
    aggression once the act is over: a. aggressive-aim; b. sexual-
    aim; *c. sex-aggression-fusion; d. impulse. (pp. 383-384)

12. Resisting this rapist generally involves little danger and can
    be quite effective. a. aggressive-aim; *b. sexual-aim; c. sex-
    aggression-fusion; d. impulse. (p. 383)

13. John has imagined Sarah's response for months; he's sure that even though she may be resistant to his advances at first, by the time he finishes, she'll be begging for more. John is a ___ rapist. a. aggressive-aim; *b. sexual-aim; c. sex-aggression-fusion; d. impulse.

14. Kanin's research on date rapes involved: a. sitting in a parked car in lover's lane and using a high powered "bug" to listen to the miscommunication going on in some of the other parked cars; b. interviewing women who had been date rape victims by getting the cooperation of college counseling centers; *c. contacting a random sample of unmarried male university students and asking them if they had made any forcible attempts at coitus while on dates; d. conducting a survey of college women via questionnaires on their experiences; e. both a & d. (p. 386)

15. When gang rape members were shown Rorschach cards, they: a. reported seeing whatever their leader had reported; b. competed for dominance to see who could find the most aggressive symbols; *c. competed for dominance to see who could find the most sexual symbols; d. exhibited strong fears of women; e. all of the above. (p. 387)

16. Hyde takes the position that rape will persist as long as: a. our society continues to give lenient sentences to convicted rapists; b. females are expected to pretend to be disinterested in sex; c. males and females play games on dates; d. all of the above; *e. both b & c. (p. 390)

True/False

1. About half of all rapes are not reported (F, p. 376).

2. At present, there is a state in which a man could be charged with statutory rape for having intercourse with a 20-year-old woman (T, p. 376).

3. The rape trauma syndrome progresses in four phases (F, p. 377).

4. Recently, some states have passed laws which do not permit the woman's previous sexual experience with people other than the rapist to be a topic during the trial (T, p. 380).

5. Judges who were interviewed about their attitudes toward rape believe that there are three categories of rape victims: genuine victims, those who engage in consensual intercourse, and those who are exhibiting female vindictiveness (T, p. 380).

6. The rape victim who escapes with only minor scratches suffers less emotional trauma than the victim who is beaten into unconsciousness (F, p. 380).

7. The less the emotional involvement between the victim and rapist, the more difficult is the victim's adjustment afterwards (F, p. 380).

8. Unfortunately, many of the changes in female socialization recommended by feminists are likely to increase females' vulnerability to rapists (F, pp. 381-382).

9. The evidence on the ratio of rapes to murders suggests that a woman's best strategy is to go limp rather than to resist the rape (F, p. 383).

10. The aggressive-aim rapist may be unable to get an erection unless the woman resists (F, p. 383).

11. The sex-aggression-fusion rapist tends to project his own confusion of sex and aggression onto his victim, saying that women are turned on by being forced and roughed-up (T, p. 384).

12. One-fourth of the males in Kanin's random sample of male university students reported having made a forceful attempt to have intercourse with their dates (T, p. 386).

13. Cases of date rape are almost always confined to casual bar pick-ups or first dates (F, p. 386).

14. Some of the men in Kanin's study of date rape were motivated by the desire to punish women whom they perceived as being "teases" or "golddiggers" (T, p. 386).

15. Those at the bottom of the dominance hierarchy in prison who get raped are called "girls" (T, p. 388).

16. Rape doesn't occur in some societies where males are socialized to be nurturant rather than aggressive (T, p. 389).

CHAPTER 17: LOVE

I. LEARNING OBJECTIVES

Study of this chapter should enable the student to:

1. Understand the various descriptions of different kinds of love that have been advanced from the Greeks up to the present.

2. Describe the approach taken by Rubin in his attempt to measure love and indicate the results of his research.

3. Describe Berscheid and Walster's two-component theory of love and indicate the extent to which research has supported their hypotheses.

4. Specify the influences on interpersonal attraction of such factors as similarity, physical appearance, proximity, and playing hard-to-get, and describe how the research on these factors was conducted.

5. Indicate the gender differences in what makes one desirable as a date and as a mate.

6. Describe the alternative choices that we have in dealing with our own jealousy.

7. Define the terms eros, agape, philia, and storge and give an example of each in your own life.

8. Compare and contrast Lewis, Maslow, Fromm & Lee in terms of their definitions of love.

II. CHAPTER AT A GLANCE

Introduction (p. 394)

Theoretical Views (pp. 394-398)
The Greeks
C. S. Lewis: Describes concepts from his book, The Four Loves.
Maslow: B-love and D-love
Fromm: The Act of Loving
John Alan Lee: Lovestyles

Research on Love (pp. 398-403)
Measuring Love: Describes Rubin's scale and research.
Love and Adrenalin: Berscheid & Walster's 2 component theory of
love.
The Schachter & Singer study
Evidence on Berscheid & Walster's theory

Interpersonal Attraction (pp. 403-408): Notes that although there
is little research on love, attraction has received extensive
research attention. This section focuses on research done by
Byrne, Walster and Rubin.
Birds of a Feather
"Hey, Good-Lookin"
From the Laboratory to Real Life
The Interpersonal Marketplace
The Girl Next Door
Playing Hard-To-Get
Evaluating the Interpersonal-Attraction Research: Points out
that its focus is on first impressions.

An Afterthought (p. 408): Notes Proxmire's criticism of research in
this area, and disagrees with him.

Summary (pp. 408-409)

Suggestions for Further Reading (p. 409)

Focus:

Jealousy (pp. 406-407): Based on Clanton & Smith's work.

III. GLOSSARY

agape. A Greek word meaning selfless love of others.

IV. AUDIO-VISUAL AIDS

Movies:

Kinds of love. Indiana University, 29 min., B & W. Describes
   various kinds of love, mistaken ideas about love, and the
   relationship between love and sex.

Tapes:

Love and intimacy. Norton, 60 min., $14.00. Love is linked with
   intimacy as a way of understanding various aspects of human
   sexuality. It is suggested that love, sex, and marriage are
   not synonymous. Presents a sensitivity session to illustrate
   the role played by intimacy in mediating between love and sex.

V. DEMONSTRATIONS OR GROUP DISCUSSION

Sentence completion: Love. The purpose of this exercise is to
have students explore their own ideas about the nature of love and
to find out what others think.
   Have students individually respond to a sentence completion exercise such as the following:

1. Love is _____.
2. If I love someone, I _____.
3. If someone loves me, they _____.
4. When you're in love, you feel _____.
5. If I am in love with someone, other possible dates seem
   _____.
6. When I am 50, I will love my spouse _____.
7. "Love at first sight" is _____.
8. Love and sex _____.
9. If I were to define "love" I would say _____.

After students have completed the form, divide the class into groups
of 6-8 students. Students should read their responses individually.
After all the responses by each student have been read, have the
group discuss what this person believes about the nature of love,
as reflected in the responses. After this has been done for all
students, the group may want to discuss back and forth the relative
merits and disadvantages of their various definitions of love. (If
the instructor feels that it might be too threatening for students
to read their own responses, they can be done anonymously by having
all students in a group put theirs together in a pile and then draw-
ing one out randomly to read.)

VI. EVALUATION MATERIALS

Essay or research questions

1. Describe Berscheid and Walster's two-component theory of love. How might jealousy function in their theory, and what might it's effects be on the experience of love? Finally, indicate how you would go about testing your hypothesis about the effect of jealousy on love.

2. Summarize the results of the research on at least three of the variables which have been found to influence attraction, and then describe the extent to which you believe you are influenced by each of these variables in your response to members of the other gender. (See pp. 403-408.)

Multiple choice

1. After reading the accounts of devastation and need for clothing and other supplies to a small midwestern town following the visit of a killer tornado, you feel overwhelmed by a sense of connection and compassion so you organize a clothing drive to help. This is an expression of: *a. agape; b. eros; c. philia; d. storge; e. ludus. (pp. 394-395)

2. You and your room mate in the dorm get along very well during your freshman year and so you decide to room together this year, as well. You correspond with each other over the summer and when you first see each other in the fall, you are genuinely delighted to see each other and you embrace happily. This is an expression of: a. agape; b. eros; *c. philia; d. storge; e. ludus. (pp. 394-395)

3. Eros refers to ___ love. *a. passionate; b. parent-child affectionate; c. friendship and comradely; d. selfless-giving. (pp. 394-395)

4. According to C. S. Lewis, the least physical of the kinds of love is: a. affection or storge; *b. philia; c. eros; d. "charity" or agape. (p. 395)

5. Maslow suggested that ___ occurs between two self-actualized people who are independent yet appreciative of each other. a. A-love (affectionate love); *b. B-love (Being love); c. C-love (Compassionate love): d. D-love (Deficiency love); e. E-love (Ecstatic love). (p. 396)

6. According to Fromm, mature love is characterized by: a. care; b. responsibility; c. respect; d. knowledge; *e. all of the above. (p. 396)

7. According to Lee, with ludus (playful love) the lovers: a. refuse to get too attached to each other; b. show great interest in improving sexual techniques; c. show little interest in improving sexual techniques; d. both a & b; *e. both a & c. (p. 397)

8. ___ has developed an operational definition of love. a. Fromm; b. Lee; *c. Rubin; d. Maslow; e. Lewis. (p. 398)

9. In Rubin's measure, ___ is NOT one of the three major components of love. a. affiliative and dependency needs; *b. respect and admiration; c. a predisposition to help; d. exclusiveness and absorption. (p. 400)

10. In Rubin's measure, love scores (the tendency to report feeling love for one's partner) were: a. higher among males; b. higher among females; *c. almost identical for males and females; d. highly correlated with liking scores for males and females; e. both b and d. (p. 400)

11. In Berscheid and Walster's theory of love, the two components are: *a. physiological arousal and appropriate labeling; b. psychological arousal and physiological arousal; c. mutual concern and physiological arousal; d. romantic feelings and mutual concern. (p. 401)

12. Berscheid and Walster's two component theory of love is based on the work of: a. Fromm; b. Rubin; *c. Schachter; d. Lee; e. Maslow. (p. 401)

13. In support of Berscheid and Walster's theory of love, research indicates that attraction toward a woman is greater among men who: a. are relaxed than among men who are in a state of fear; *b. are in a state of fear than among men who are relaxed; c. have just finished a large meal than among men who are hungry; d. are happy than among men who are depressed. (pp. 402-403)

14. The effect of physical attractiveness on popularity is: a. equally strong for men and for women; b. stronger for men than for women; *c. stronger for women than for men; d. very weak for men and for women. (p. 404)

15. When Byrne and his colleagues attempted to examine the influence of similarity and physical attractiveness on popularity in a real-life setting, they found that: a. physical attractiveness had a strong influence, but similarity of attitudes was rather unimportant; b. similarity of attitudes had a strong influence but physical attractiveness was rather unimportant; *c. both factors had a strong influence on popularity, thus extending the results of work in the lab to the "real" world; d. neither factor had much of an influence on popularity. (p. 404)

16. Results of a number of studies have found that desirability as a date and as a mate is determined by: a. physical attractiveness for both men and women; b. competence or success for both men and women; c. physical attractiveness for women and physical size for men; *d. physical attractiveness for women and success for men. (pp. 404-405)

17. The song "The more I see you, the more I love you," is: *a. supported by research in that repeated exposure to someone increases our attraction to them; b. not supported by research, as we appear to be more attracted to what is novel; c. an idea Hyde cites as badly in need of research attention; d. supported by research with adolescents, but not supported with adults. (p. 405)

18. Sarah is really turned on by Joe, and when he unexpectedly calls and asks her to go get a beer with him, she's elated. In terms of increasing his interest in her, her best bet is to: a. refuse, saying that she has to study; b. refuse nonchalantly, saying she's already got a date; *c. accept, saything that although she should be studying and has already turned down several invitations, she'd love to go with him; d. accept, and then make a point of being very friendly to several other male friends at the bar. (pp. 405-408)

19. In applying the research on interpersonal attraction to your own life, you should be aware that the influence of such variables as appearance and similarity: a. has been explored mainly with couples who've known each other for some time; *b. has been explored mainly with strangers or couples who didn't know one another very well; c. is limited to our first impressions; d. only holds for couples who have been involved for some time. (p. 408)

20. Regarding jealousy, Clanton and Smith have: *a. suggested that we can choose whether to handle it in a defensive or constructive manner; b. conducted experiments which demonstrate that we feel more love toward a partner who exhibits jealousy; c. conducted experiments which demonstrate that we are repelled by jealous behavior in a partner; d. conducted research which demonstrates that jealousy is innate rather than learned. (pp. 406-407)

True/False

1. Storge is the Greek term for the kind of affection felt between parent and child (T, pp. 394-395).

2. Philia is the Greek term for selfless, giving love (F, pp. 394-395).

3. C. S. Lewis argues that philia (or friendship) can rarely exist between a man and a woman in a strictly gender-role-stereotyped society (T, p. 395).

4. According to Maslow, being lovers are independent and disinterested, but eager to help the other toward self-actualization (T, p. 396).

5. In The Art of Loving, Fromm argued that love is something one is in, not something one does (F, p. 396).

6. For Fromm, mature love involves a symbiotic union between two people (F, p. 396).

7. Fromm believes that erotic love is exclusive and fairly permanent (T, p. 397).

8. Lee believes that many conflicts arise when two different types of lovers are paired with each other (T, p. 398).

9. In his research on love, Rubin found that we have a very strong tendency to like the person we love (F, p. 400).

10. Rubin found that men tend to like their girlfriends more than women like their boyfriends (F, p. 400).

11. In Rubin's research, couples with different religious faiths tend to love one another more than couples with the same religious faith (T, p. 400-401).

12. In Berscheid and Walster's theory, the physical arousal that is important for love may be the result of either pleasant or unpleasant stimuli (T, p. 403).

13. The old adage "opposites attract" is supported by the results of research on attraction by Byrne and his colleagues (F, pp. 403-404).

14. Although similarity of attitudes appears to be a very important determinant of attraction in laboratory research, we have no data regarding its influence in real-life situations (F, p. 404).

15. Unattractive women rate high status men as much more desirable than attractive women do (F, p. 405).

16. A prostitute who plays hard-to-get is paid more by her customer than one who plays easy-to-get (F, p. 405).

17. The research on interpersonal attraction has been conducted mainly with couples who have been committed to one another for some time (F, p. 408).

18. Clanton and Smith suggest that jealousy has two forms one of which is a relatively mild and harmless feeling of being left out while the more serious form is a persistant fear of loss (T, p. 406).

CHAPTER 18: SEXUAL DYSFUNCTION AND SEX THERAPY

I. LEARNING OBJECTIVES

Study of this chapter should enable the student to:

1. Name and describe each of the major male and female sexual dysfunctions and indicate how common each is as a complaint among those seeking sex therapy.

2. Know the extent to which learned vs. organic (physical) factors contribute to the causes of each of the dysfunctions.

3. Describe how the various diseases and/or drugs and medicines affect sexual functioning, and indicate the effects of handicaps on sexual functioning.

4. Compare and contrast the different approaches to sex therapy in terms of their basic assumptions, treatment procedures, length of treatment, and success rates.

5. Describe the problems with some of the terms used to describe sexual dysfunctions.

6. Contrast traditional vs. current definitions of the sexual functioning of a woman who has orgasm through masturbation, manual stimulation and/or oral stimulation, but who does not have orgasms in vaginal intercourse.

7. Describe the influence of marijuana on both sexual experience and sexual functioning, and describe the ways in which alcohol varies in its effect on sexual functioning.

8. Describe the specific ways in which prior learning and immediate causes can influence sexual functioning.

9. Specify Masters & Johnson's beliefs about the use of cotherapists and the effect of transference in sex therapy, and describe the criticisms that have been made of their work and conclusions.

10. Describe the advice Hyde gives regarding both the prevention and "cure" of sexual dysfunction.

11. Define the terms dyspareunia, phimosis, Kegel exercises, spectatoring, surrogate, sensate focus, squeeze technique, and pubococcygenus muscle.

12. Indicate how Kaplan, Masters & Johnson, and LoPiccolo & Lobitz have contributed to our understanding in this area.

II. CHAPTER AT A GLANCE

Introduction (pp. 412-413): Defines sexual dysfunction, notes that we don't know its incidence in the general population, but gives Masters & Johnson's estimate.

Kinds of Sexual Dysfunction (pp. 413-417)
   Erectile Dysfunction (Impotence): Distinguishes between primary and secondary erectile dysfunction, deals with incidence, and negative aspects of the term "impotence", difference between potency and fertility and responses to the problem.
   Premature Ejaculation: Describes various definitions, incidence and responses to the problem.
   Retarded Ejaculation: Definition, incidence, and responses.
   Orgasmic Dysfunction: Distinguishes between primary and secondary variants, and notes negative connotation of the term "frigidity". Discusses Freud's distinction between clitoral and vaginal orgasm and Masters & Johnson's debunking of the distinction. Gives incidence.
   Vaginismus: Definition and incidence.
   Painful Intercourse: Defined.
   Sexual Apathy

What Causes Sexual Dysfunction? (pp. 417-427)
   Organic Causes
      Erectile dysfunction
      Premature ejaculation
      Retarded ejaculation
      Orgasmic dysfunction in women
      Painful intercourse
      Vaginismus
   Drugs: Covers medicines and psychedelics.
   Psychological Causes
      Immediate causes: Includes anxiety, construction of barriers to erotic pleasure, communication failure and ineffective stimulation.
      Prior learning: Includes traumatic first intercourse, seductive parents, association between sex and sin, parental punishment for masturbation, etc., double-standard. Discussion of problem of determining "causes" of the dysfunction without adequate control groups.
      Marital conflict: Notes sex as the symptom rather than cause.
      Intrapsychic conflict: Description of Psychoanalytic viewpoint.
   Sexuality and the Handicapped
      Sexuality and the spinal-cord-injured

The Masters and Johnson Sex Therapy Program (pp. 427-432)
   The Format and Basic Principles: Notes that Masters & Johnson use a behavior therapy model, describes their goals, use of cotherapists, demand that both partners participate, their attitude regarding "transference", and their use of surrogates.

Basic Therapy Techniques: Includes education, sensate focus
    exercises.
The Success Rate

Other Therapies (pp. 432-438)
    Variations on the Masters and Johnson Method: Notes expense
        involved in Masters and Johnson's program, gives references
        to Kaplan's and to Hartman & ithian's books.
    Specific Treatment for Specific Problems
        Kegel exercises
        Squeeze technique
        Masturbation: Describes LoPiccolo & Lobitz's program.
    Marital Therapy
    Individual Psychotherapy
    Which Therapy is Best?: Says that it depends on the problem.

Some Practical Advice (pp. 438-439)
    Avoiding Sexual Dysfunction: Hyde's recommendations.
    Picking a Sex Therapist

Summary (pp. 439-440)

Suggestions for Further Reading (p. 440)

Focuses:

    A Case of Orgasmic Dysfunction in a Woman (pp. 418-419)
    The Schedule of Treatment in the Masters and Johnson Therapy
        Program (pp. 428-429)
    A Case of Erectile Dysfunction in a Man (pp. 436-437)

III. GLOSSARY

    anorgasmia. The inability of a woman to orgasm; a sexual dys-
        function.

    coitus reservatus. Sexual intercourse in which the man inten-
        tionally refrains from ejaculating.

    dyspareunia. Painful intercourse.

    erectile dysfunction. The inability to get or maintain an
        erection.

    frigidity. Lack of sexual response in a woman.

    intromission. Insertion of the penis into the vagina.

    premature ejaculation. A sexual dysfunction in which the male
        ejaculates too soon.

prenatal. Before birth.

priapism. A rare condition in which erections are long-lasting and painful.

retarded ejaculation. A sexual dysfunction in which the male cannot have an orgasm, even though he is highly aroused.

retrograde ejaculation. A condition in which orgasm in the male is not accompanied by an external ejaculation; instead, the ejaculate goes into the urinary bladder.

sensate focus exercises. Exercises prescribed by sex therapists to increase sexual response.

sexual dysfunction. A problem with sexual responding that causes a person mental distress; examples are erectile dysfunction in men and anorgasmia in women.

IV. AUDIO-VISUAL AIDS

Movies:

Female sexological examination. Center for Marital and Sexual Studies, 25 min., color, $395/$65. Depicts Hartman & Fithian's procedure from their research on non-orgasmic women.

Female masturbation - Justine. Center for Marital and Sexual Studies, 16 min., color, $275/$60. Shows a female pleasuring her body including her genitalia while looking at herself in a mirror. She experiments with several vibrators and has a pronounced orgasm. Purpose of film is to help women to know themselves sexually and improve their sexual response in penile-vaginal intercourse.

Non-demand pleasuring. CMSS, 23 min., color, $275/$45. Shows three positions which are useful in treating premature ejaculators, "impotent" males, and pre-orgasmic females.

Like other people. Perennial, #1007, 37 min., $375/$37.50. Although this film takes quite a large proportion of class time to deal with a somewhat tangential topic in the chapter - the sexual needs and feelings of the mentally and physically handicapped - it is well worth it. Both the first author and the students who previewed this film were moved to tears by the sensitivity and beauty of the interaction between two palsied lovers. Discussion in the film of reproduction, birth control problems and desire for intimacy - all of which are frequently blocked by the institutions in which such people are incarcerated - provides an excellent springboard for class discussion of these issues. This is a _superb_ film.

V. DEMONSTRATIONS OR GROUP DISCUSSION

A. Guest speaker: Sex therapist. Invite a sex therapist to speak to the class on the kinds of therapy techniques she or he uses, and answer any questions students have about sex therapy.

B. Communication role play. The purpose of this exercise is to help students learn to communicate openly with their partners about their sexual feelings and sexual needs (which is part of the sex therapy process, and is also good preventive sex therapy).

Have students break into groups of 6-8 and do either or both of the following role plays (see the General Instructions for Role Plays in Chapter 14 of this Manual):

Situation I. Kathy and Tom are both 23 and have been married for 1 year. Kathy feels that Tom does not show enough concern for her needs when they make love. Foreplay is too brief and not caring enough, and she doesn't get the kind of stimulation she needs; probably as a result, she rarely has an orgasm, although Tom does not seem to realize this. Otherwise, their marriage is happy. Role play Kathy communicating her concerns to Tom.

Situation II. Carol and Mark are both 30 and have been married 5 years. Mark is dissatisfied with their lovemaking because Carol is so unresponsive. Though she never refuses when he initiates sex, she never initiates it herself. When they make love, she lies there passively, does little to stimulate him, and gives no evidence that she enjoys it. Role play Mark communicating his concerns to Carol.

More daring instructors may wish to try role-playing some nonverbal communication, which is similar to the sensate focus of pleasuring exercises used by sex therapists. Have students work in pairs. Have one member of the pair (the giving partner) stroke the other person's (the getting partner) arm. The getting partner should communicate nonverbally what kind of stroking is most pleasant by placing their hand on the giving partner's and guiding it. The partners should then switch roles, and try different kinds of stroking (slow, fast, hard pressure, soft pressure), always communicating nonverbally what is most pleasant. Finally, the partners may practice expressing different emotions--such as tenderness, caring, anger, impatience, lack of caring--by touching. They may also practice using verbal feedback in communicating what kinds of touch they prefer.

VI. EVALUATION MATERIALS

Essay or research questions

1. How do drugs (sedatives, alcohol, barbiturates, psychedelics, etc.) affect sexual functioning (See pp. 420-423.)

2. Why should we be cautious in generalizing Masters & Johnson's data on the causes of sexual dysfunction. (See pp. 424-425.) Select one of the dysfunctions, describe their conclusions with respect to the cause of the dysfunction; and indicate how you would go about gathering more rigorous evidence in an attempt to explain the cause.

3. Hyde offers four pieces of practical advice for a good relationship. Describe these. (See pp. 438-439.) Indicate which of the four you think you would (or do) find most problematic and why.

Multiple choice

1. Masters & Johnson suggest that ___ of the marriages are either sexually dysfunctional or will be in the near future. a. 10%; b. 25%; *c. 50%; d. 75%. (p. 412)

2. With ___, a man has difficulty getting or maintaining an erection but has been able to have vaginal or anal intercourse at least once. a. primary sterility; b. primary impotence; c. secondary sterility; *d. secondary impotence. (p. 413)

3. The most frequent male dysfunction found by Masters & Johnson was: a. premature ejaculation; b. primary impotence; *c. secondary impotence; d. retarded ejaculation. (p. 413)

4. Premature ejaculation was the ___ common sexual dysfunction found by Masters & Johnson. a. most; *b. second most; c. third most; d. fourth most. (p. 414)

5. Masters & Johnson refer to this dysfunction as ejaculatory incompetence: a. premature ejaculation; *b. retarded ejaculation; c. primary impotence; d. secondary impotence; e. orgasmic dysfunction. (p. 415)

6. The scientific term for the condition in women who have never had an orgasm is: a. frigidity; *b. primary orgasmic dysfunction; c. secondary orgasmic dysfunction; d. retarded ejaculation; e. vaginismus. (p. 415)

7. The most common sexual dysfunction among women seeking help from Masters & Johnson is: a. vaginismus; *b. orgasmic dysfunction; c. painful intercourse; d. sexual apathy. (p. 416)

8. Dyspareunia is: a. vaginismus; *b. painful intercourse; c. primary orgasmic dysfunction; d. secondary orgasmic dysfunction. (p. 416)

9. ___ refers to a spastic contraction of the outer third of the vagina. *a. vaginismus; b. dyspareunia; c. painful intercourse; d. orgasmic dysfunction. (p. 416)

10. The dysfunction that is most likely to be caused by physical (organic) rather than psychological factors is: a. premature ejaculation; b. orgasmic dysfunction; c. erectile dysfunction; *d. painful intercourse. (p. 420).

11. ___ of the cases of sexual dysfunction result directly from organic factors. *a. 10-20%; b. 30-40%; c. 60-70%; d. 80-90%. (p. 417)

12. Erectile dysfunction is associated with: a. heart and circulatory system diseases; b. diabetes; c. spinal cord damage; d. both a & c; *e. all of the above. (p. 418)

13. According to Hyde, Parkinson's disease sometimes causes: a. premature ejaculation; b. erectile dysfunction; *c. retarded ejaculation; d. all of the above. (p. 420)

14. Dyspareunia may be caused by: a. vaginal entrance disorders; b. clitoral damage or irritation; c. vaginal infections; d. pelvic disorders; *e. all of the above. (p. 420)

15. Frequent marijuana use: a. is unrelated to testosterone level; b. is associated with temporary lowering of testosterone levels; c. is associated with permanent lowering of testosterone levels; d. is associated with lowered sperm count; *e. both b & d. (p. 421)

16. "Dry orgasm" (orgasm without ejaculate) appears to be a side effect of: *a. some drugs used for treating schizophrenia; b. tranquillizers; c. anti-depressants; d. marijuana; e. all of the above. (p. 421)

17. Masters & Johnson's evidence regarding the effects of early experiences, religious training, parental punishment, etc. on the development of sexual dysfunction in adulthood comes from their: a. experimental research; b. work with animals; *c. clinical observations; d. surveys of college students. (p. 424)

18. Spectatoring refers to: a. people who get sexually aroused from watching nudes or sexual acts; *b. being an observer of one's own sexual performance; c. a biological cause of sexual dysfunction; d. lack of communication that creates dysfunction. (p. 423)

19. The view that all sexual problems are caused by unresolved
    Oedipal problems was advanced by: a. Kaplan; b. Masters & John-
    son; *c. Freud; d. Ellis. (p. 426)

20. The most effective way to produce physical arousal in the spinal-
    cord injured is to: a. stimulate them with erotic talk; b. give
    them erotic materials (books, movies, etc.); *c. physically
    stimulate their genitals; d. through hugging, kissing, and simi-
    lar signs of affection. (p. 427)

21. Masters & Johnson's overall success rate in sex therapy is:
    a. 45%; b. 62%; *c. 82%; d. 95%. (p. 431)

22. Masters & Johnson's data indicate that the dysfunction with the
    highest failure rate in therapy is: *a. primary erectile dys-
    function; b. secondary erectile dysfunction; c. premature ejacu-
    lation; d. none of the above. (p. 431)

23. The purpose of the Kegel exercise is: a. to help premature ejac-
    ulators; b. to increase couples' awareness of tactile senses;
    c. to exercise and strengthen the pubbococcygeal muscle; d. to
    increase the sensitivity of the vaginal area; *e. both c & d.
    (p. 432)

24. The squeeze technique is used to treat: a. women who's vaginal
    muscles have become weak and loose through childbirth; b. retar-
    ded ejaculation; *c. premature ejaculation; d. primary erectile
    dysfunction; e. secondary erectile dysfunction. (p. 433)

25. In 1977, the 2-week Masters & Johnson treatment cost: a. $500;
    b. $1,000; *c. $2,500; d. $5,000. (p. 432)

26. Of the three basic therapy approaches, ___ is the most effective,
    according to Hyde. a. behavior therapy; b. marital therapy.
    c. individual psychotherapy; *d. none of the above; as yet we
    have no definitive evidence suggesting which is best. (p. 438)

True/False

1. Until Masters & Johnson developed their program, almost all sexual dysfunction was treated by long-term therapy (T, p. 412).

2. A sexual dysfunction is any one of various disturbances or impair-
   ments of sexual functioning (T, p. 412).

3. Sterility refers to an inability to have or maintain an erection
   (F, p. 413).

4. Impotence is far more common among upper and middle-class males
   than among lower-class males (F, p. 413).

5. It has been estimated that ½ of the general male population has occasionally had impotence (T, p. 413).

6. Hyde defines premature ejaculation as ejaculation which occurs prior to ten pelvic thrusts (F, p. 414).

7. Orgasmic dysfunctions in women accounted for the vast majority of Masters & Johnson's female clients (T, p. 416).

8. Persistant dyspareunia was rather uncommon in Masters & Johnson's cases (T, p. 417).

9. Most cases of erectile dysfunction are due to physiological rather than psychological causes (F, p. 417).

10. The majority of diabetic men have erectile dysfunction (F, p. 419).

11. Half the cases of premature ejaculation are due to physical causes (F, p. 419).

12. Erectile dysfunction is at times the earliest symptom for developing diabetes (T, p. 418).

13. A man's erectile dysfunction is not from physical causes if he sometimes wakes in the morning with an erection (T, p. 419).

14. Orgasmic dysfunction may be effectively treated with estrogen (F, p. 420).

15. Dyspareunia is often caused by organic factors (T, p. 420).

16. Poor hygiene can cause painful intercourse in men (T, p. 420).

17. Phimosis is a condition in which the foreskin cannot be retracted (T, p. 420).

18. A small amount of alcohol may reduce anxiety, thus improving sex response (T, p. 421).

19. Research on marijuana use, testosterone and sperm count suggests that the observed relationship may be quickly reversed when marijuana use is stopped (T, p. 421).

20. Most of Masters & Johnson's evidence on the causes of sexual dysfunction come from experimental data (F, p. 424).

21. About 10% of U.S. adults have physical handicaps that impose substantial limits on their activities (T, p. 426).

22. Spinal-cord injured women generally experience vaginal lubrication and orgasm similar to that of able-bodied women (F, p. 427).

23. Some spinal-injured women are able to become pregnant and carry a baby to term (T, p. 427).

24. One of the basic goals of Masters & Johnson's therapy is to help clients develop goal-oriented sexual performance (F, p. 427).

25. A complete medical examination of the couple must precede their participation in Masters & Johnson's 2-week therapy program (F, p. 428).

26. Masters & Johnson view the use of transference as very important to the success of their treatment (F, p. 428).

27. The success rate in treating sexual dysfunction is higher when both spouses participate than when the client works with a surrogate (F, p. 430).

28. Males, unlike females, have a fixed number of orgasms they can have in a lifetime without damaging their cardiovascular system (F, p. 431).

29. Sex therapy is not yet covered by any major medical health insurance programs (F, p. 432).

30. The stop-start technique is used in the treatment of secondary orgasmic dysfunction in women (F, p. 434).

31. Data indicate that masturbation is the technique most likely to produce orgasm in women (T, p. 434).

Fill in the blank

Give the name of the sexual dysfunction in the blank space next to its definition.

1. _____ : The inability to postpone ejaculation until the man has decided he wants to ejaculate.

2. _____ : Inability for a woman to have an orgasm.

3. _____ : Spastic contractions of the outer third of the vagina.

4. _____ : The inability to have or maintain an erection.

5. _____ : Inability to ejaculate, even though the man has a solid erection and has had more than enough stimulation.

6. _____ : Experiencing pain in the vagina, clitoris, penis or deep in the pelvis.

Answer key: 1. premature ejaculation; 2. orgasmic dysfunction; 3. vaginismus; 4. erectile dysfunction; 5. retarded ejaculation; 6. painful intercourse or dyspareunia.

CHAPTER 19: SEXUAL DISEASES

I. LEARNING OBJECTIVES

Study of this chapter should enable the student to:

1. Describe the incidence of each of the sexual diseases and indicate which are on the increase in the U.S.

2. Compare and contrast each of the diseases in terms of their symptoms, how they are diagnosed, and how they are treated.

3. Specify steps which may be taken to prevent each disease or reduce the likelihood of catching it.

4. Indicate which groups seem to be most and least likely to get breast, cervical, and prostate cancers.

5. Give, in detail, methods for individuals to increase their chances of detecting each of the cancers early.

6. Describe the historical origins of syphilis and gonorrhea.

7. Indicate how males and females differ in their symptoms at various stages of syphilis and the other diseases.

8. Specify ways in which women can prevent vaginitis.

9. Describe transmission, diagnosis and treatment for the non-sexually transmitted genital infections and inflammations.

10. Describe the various treatments for breast cancer and for the other cancers.

11. Indicate the factors which have contributed to the current status of gonorrhea among the communicable diseases.

12. Define salpingitis, Gram-stain, Treponema pallidum, Wasserman, mastectomy and Pap test.

II. CHAPTER AT A GLANCE

<u>Introduction</u> (p. 442): Notes that generally gynecologists treat VD in women, and urologists or dermatologists treat it in men.

<u>Gonorrhea</u> (pp. 442-445): Gives historical and sociological background. Points out current epidemic and factors responsible for it.
<u>Symptoms</u>
<u>Treatment</u>

<u>Syphilis</u> (pp. 445-451): Gives historical background.
<u>Symptoms</u>
<u>Diagnosis</u>
<u>Treatment</u>

<u>Other Diseases of Sexual Transmission</u> (pp. 451-453)
<u>Nonspecific Urethritis</u>
<u>Chancroid</u>
<u>Lymphogranuloma Venereum</u>
<u>Granuloma Inguinale</u>
<u>Venereal Warts</u>
<u>Herpes Genitalis</u>
<u>Pubic Lice</u>

<u>Preventing VD</u> (pp. 453-454): Notes that some contraceptives help (condom, foam) and describes hygiene practices to decrease risk.

<u>Other Inflamations</u> (pp. 454-456)
<u>Monilia</u>
<u>Trichomoniasis</u>
<u>Nonspecific Vaginitis</u>
<u>Cystitis</u>

<u>Cancer of the Sex Organs</u> (pp. 456-462)
<u>Breast Cancer</u>
<u>Diagnosis</u>
<u>Mastectomy</u>
<u>Cancer of the Cervix</u>
<u>Cancer of the Prostate</u>

<u>Summary</u> (pp. 462-463)

<u>Suggestions for Further Reading</u> (p. 463)

<u>Focuses</u>:

<u>Preventing Vaginitis</u> (p. 455)
<u>The Breast Self-Exam</u> (p. 458)

III. GLOSSARY

Candida albicans. A yeast or fungus in the vagina; if its growth gets out of control, it causes vaginitis, or irritation of the vagina, with an accompanying discharge.

chancre. A painless open sore with a hard ridge around it; it is an early symptom of syphilis.

chancroid. A venereal disease.

crabs. See pediculosis pubis.

cystitis. Inflammation of the urinary bladder; the major symptom is a burning sensation while urinating.

gonorrhea. A common venereal disease.

granuloma inguinale. A rare venereal disease.

herpes genitalis. A disease characterized by painful bumps on the genitals.

impotence. See erectile dysfunction.

lymphogranuloma venereum (LGV). A virus-caused disease affecting the lymph glands in the genital region.

monilia. A yeast infection of the vagina.

Pediculosis pubis. Lice attaching themselves to the roots of the pubic hair; "crabs".

prophylactic. A drug or device used to prevent disease, often specifically venereal disease.

pubic lice. See pediculosis pubis.

spirochete. A spiral-shaped bacterium; one kind causes syphilis.

syphilis. A venereal disease.

trichomoniasis. A vaginal infection.

vaginismus. A strong, spastic contraction of the muscles around the vagina, closing off the vaginal entrance and making entercourse impossible.

vaginitis. An inflammation or irritation of the vagina, usually due to infection.

<u>venereal disease</u>. A disease transmitted primarily by secual
    intercourse.

<u>Wassermann test</u>. A blood test for syphilis.

IV. AUDIO-VISUAL AIDS

Movies:

<u>Venereal diseases</u>. Media Guild, 17 min., color, $255/$25.
    Covers both psychological and medical issues regarding VD
    through interviews between a doctor and patients afflicted
    with the symptoms of gonorrhea and syphilis. Shows the doc-
    tor examining the patients and describes symptoms, diagnosis
    and treatment. Emphasis on debunking both the myths and the
    shame traditionally associated with VD.

<u>When love needs care</u>. Perennial, 13 min., color, $175/$17.50.
    Via a documentary style, this film shows two young people
    visiting a doctor's office for examination and treatment for
    VD. Again, attempts to debunk myths and shame.

<u>Pelvic and breast examination</u>. Perennial, 12 min., color, $175/
    $17.50. A young woman performs the breast exam, and the pro-
    cedures and purposes of a pelvic exam are shown. Demonstrates
    how pap smears and gonorrhea cultures are taken.

V. DEMONSTRATIONS OR GROUP DISCUSSION

   <u>Guest lecture - VD clinic</u>. If you have a VD clinic in your area,
they may provide you with a speaker who can describe the situation
in your community regarding the incidence of the various venereal
diseases, the extent to which the clinic maintains confidentiality,
the costs for their service, the age range of their clients, etc.
If you have no VD clinic, you might try asking a gynecologist and/or
urologist if he/she would be willing to speak.

VI. EVALUATION MATERIALS

Essay or research questions

1. Your cousin calls you because she knows you're taking the sex
course, and she's just returned from an afternoon skinny-dipping
spree with George. She likes him very much and he's planning to
come over for the evening, but she's concerned about the possibility
that he might have VD, because she noticed something "funny" about
his penis. How would you advise her (a) to tell whether or not he
has VD, and which one, and (b) to deal with George about her concern

that he has VD and her reluctance to have intercourse, given Hyde's suggestions. (See pp. 443, 447-449, 454.)

2. Describe what you can do to decrease the chances of catching VD (aside from keeping your chastity belt locked). (See p. 454.)

3. Give five methods of reducing the risk of vaginitis. (See p. 455.)

4. As your text noted, 1 out of every 15 women gets breast cancer. Imagine that you or a friend of yours discovers a lump while doing the monthly breast exam. First, describe the procedures likely to be used by a doctor to diagnose the lump. Second, describe the potential psychological impact of mastectomy, should that be necessary, and indicate what can be done to decrease the associated depression. (See pp. 457-461.)

Multiple choice

1. The gonococcus was first identified during: a. the latter half of the 1700's; b. the first half of the 1800's; *c. the latter half of the 1800's; d. the first half of the 1900's. (p. 442)

2. Which of the following is not true? Epidemic gonorrhea: a. occurred during WWI; b. occurred during WWII; *c. has been virtually eliminated since the 1950's with the use of penicillan; d. is occurring at present. (p. 443)

3. It is currently estimated that ___ of American young people will contract gonorrhea or syphilis by the time they are 25. a. one tenth; b. one quarter; *c. one half; d. three quarters. (p. 443)

4. Most reported gonorrhea infections occur in the ___ age group. a. 15-19; b. 20-29; *c. 15-29; d. 25-39; e. none of these; gonorrhea occurs about equally in all age groups of sexually active people. (p. 443)

5. Gonorrhea symptoms may appear as early as ___ after sex with an infected partner. *a. the first day; b. the third day; c. one week; d. one month. (p. 443)

6. About ___% of women infected with gonorrhea are asymptomatic during the early stages. a. 20; b. 40; c. 60; *d. 80; e. 98. (p. 444)

7. Mary and John are about to have intercourse, when Mary notices a thick yellowish discharge coming out of his penis, which is possibly due to: a. chancroid; b. herpes genitalis; c. nonspecific urethritis; *d. gonorrhea; e. syphilis. (pp. 443, 447, 451)

8. Josie is playing with Jack's penis when she feels an area like a crater with a hard, raised edge. She asks if it hurts, and he says no. Jack probably has: a. chancroid; b. herpes genitalis; c. nonspecific urethritis; d. gonorrhea; *e. syphilis. (pp. 443, 447, 451)

9. Morton winces in pain while Suzanne is fondling his genitals and she realizes that she has touched a round, raised, soft rim of a sore. Morton probably has: *a. chancroid; b. herpes genitalis; c. nonspecific urethritis; d. gonorrhea; e. syphilis. (pp. 443, 447, 451)

10. The primary site of gonorrhea infection in women is the: a. clitoris; b. vagina; *c. cervix; d. uterus. (p. 444)

11. Gonorrhea can infect: a. the genital and reproductive organs; b. the mouth and throat; c. the anus and rectum; d. the eyes; *e. all of the above. (p. 444)

12. Diagnosis of gonorrhea by treating a smear of the discharge with Gram-stain is: a. highly accurate; b. used only for men; c. used only for women; d. highly accurate for men, but somewhat inaccurate for women; *e. somewhat accurate for men but highly inaccurate for women. (p. 445)

13. Treatment for gonorrhea is usually two doses of 2.4 million units of penicillan injected in the buttocks: *a. and this treatment is highly effective; b. which is smaller than the dose given for syphilis; c. in order to punish the patient; d. which is twice the dose required 20 years ago. (p. 445)

14. Syphilis is named for: a. the person who isolated the causal bacterium; *b. the shepherd Syphilis who got VD for violating the will of the Sun God; c. the town in which the first VD epidemic in recorded history occurred; d. the French hospital providing a center for VD victims. (p. 447)

15. Syphilis ranks ___ among the most common communicable diseases. a. first; b. second; c. third; *d. fourth; e. fifth. (p. 447)

16. An early symptom of syphilis is the chancre, which: a. is very painful; b. appears as early as 3 days after sex with an infected person; *c. has a hard, raised edge; d. all of the above. (p. 447)

17. A generalized body rash appears in ___ syphilis. a. primary stage; *b. secondary stage; c. latent; d. late; e. fatal. (p. 448)

18. ___ symptomatic of second stage syphilis. a. Hair loss is; b. Sore throat and headaches are; c. Muscle, bone, and joint pains are; d. A low persistant fever is; *e. all of the above. (p. 449)

19. There are no symptoms during ___ syphilis. a. primary stage; b. secondary stage; *c. latent; d. late. (p. 449)

20. If a syphilitic mother is diagnosed and treated before the ___ of pregnancy, the child will not develop the disease. a. beginning; b. second month; *c. fourth month; d. sixth month; e. end of. (p. 450)

21. The VDRL blood test: a. is useful for mass screening; b. correctly diagnoses only about 75% of the cases of primary syphilis; c. is completely accurate in detecting secondary stage syphilis; d. gives "false positives" to people who have recently had measles or chicken-pox; *e. all of the above. (pp. 450-451)

22. World wide, the incidence of ___ is increasing even faster than that of gonorrhea. a. syphilis; b. chancroid; *c. nonspecific urethritis; d. herpes genitalis; e. lymphogranuloma venereum. (p. 451)

23. With mild pain in urinating and a thin, clear or slightly white discharge, ___ is suspected. a. syphilis; b. herpes genitalis; c. lymphogranuloma venereum; *d. nonspecific urethritis. (p. 451)

24. Tetracycline is not the major treatment for: a. nonspecific urethritis; *b. trichomoniasis; c. lymphogranuloma venereum; d. granuloma inguinale; e. all of the above. (p.

25. Chancroid is difficult to diagnose because it may be confused with: a. syphilis; b. lymphogranuloma vereneum; c. gonorrhea; d. all of the above; *e. both a & b. (p. 451)

26. Elephantiasis can result from untreated: a. chancroid; *b. lymphogranuloma venereum; c. granuloma inguinale; d. herpes genitalis; e. trichomoniasis. (p. 452)

27. The major long term risk associated with herpes genitalis is: *a. cervical cancer; b. brain lesions; c. blood clotting; d. sterility. (p. 452)

28. Thrush in babies can result from birth to a mother having: a. gonorrhea; b. lymphogranuloma venereum; c. herpes genitalis; *d. monilia; e. syphilis. (p. 454)

29. There are usually no symptoms in the male with: a. herpes genitalis; *b. trichomoniasis; c. venereal warts; d. nonspecific urethritis. (p. 455)

30. One can get ___ from toilets: a. syphilis; b. gonorrhea; *c. trichomoniasis; d. all of the above. (p. 455)

31. Breast cancer strikes 1 in ___ American women. a. 5; *b. 15; c. 25; d. 50. (p. 457)

32. ___ % of breast lumps are benign. a. 20; b. 40; c. 60; *d. 80. (p. 457)

33. Unfortunately, ___ has a very high rate of false positives in breast cancer diagnosis. a. needle aspiration; b. mammogram; *c. thermography; d. xeroradiography. (p. 457)

34. Which does not belong here? a. radical mastectomy; *b. thermography; c. chemotherapy; d. lumpectomy. (pp. 458, 460)

35. Cervical cancer is the ___ common form of female cancer. a. most; *b. second most; c. fourth most; d. sixth most. (p. 461)

36. Cancer of the ___ is more common than cervical cancer. a. vulva; b. vagina; *c. breast; d. uterus; e. ovaries. (p. 456)

37. ___ is not an early symptom of prostate cancer. a. frequent urination; *b. decrease in frequency of erections; c. difficulty in urination; d. increase in sex drive. (p. 462)

True/False

1. VD in women is generally treated by urologists (F, p. 442).

2. Among the communicable diseases, gonorrhea is second only to the common cold in prevalence (T, p. 443).

3. Use of the pill decreases susceptibility to gonorrhea (F, p. 443)

4. You must have sexual relations with a partner who is infected with gonorrhea in order to get it yourself (T, p. 443).

5. Gonorrhea symptoms generally take about 3 weeks to appear after sex with an infected person (F, p. 443).

6. Untreated gonorrhea can cause sterility in both men and women (T, pp. 443-444).

7. Asymptomatic gonorrhea is fairly common in males (F, p. 443).

8. Gonorrhea can be contracted by mouth-to-mouth kissing (F, p. 443).

9. The eyes of an infant born to a mother with gonorrhea may be destroyed within days of birth if left untreated (T, p. 444).

10. Gonorrhea is diagnosed with a highly accurate blood test (F, p. 445).

11. Pregnant women with gonorrhea should be given tetracycline instead of penicillin (F, p. 445).

12. Supporters of the evolutionary theory of the origins of syphilis point to the fact that the organisms causing yaws and syphilis are indistinguishable (T, p. 446).

13. Until the 19th century, it was thought that syphilis and gonorrhea were a single disease (T, p. 447).

14. The Wasserman test was used for diagnosis of gonorrhea (F, p. 447).

15. Syphilis is more common and less lethal than gonorrhea (F, p. 447).

16. Syphilis is presently increasing to epidemic proportions (F, p. 447).

17. It is possible to get syphilis by touching the chancre of an infected person (T, p. 448).

18. The appearance of a rash on the palms of the hands or the soles of the feet is a particularly distinctive symptom of syphilis (T, p. 448).

19. The person remains contagious throughout latent stage syphilis although there are no symptoms (F, p. 449).

20. The VDRL blood test for syphilis does not give accurate results until at least 4-6 weeks after the person has been infected (T, p. 450).

21. The gonorrhea bacterium is more fragile than the syphilis bacterium (F, p. 451).

22. The surrounding rim of the sores in chancroid are soft (T, p. 451).

23. A thin clear discharge from the penis is a symptom of syphilis (F, p. 451).

24. There is no known antibiotic to kill herpes genitalis (T, p. 453).

25. Diagnosis of nonspecific vaginitis occurs when there is a vaginal infection with accompanying discharge, but no cause can be found (T, p. 456).

26. Cystitis occurs a bit more frequently in women than in men (F, p. 456).

27. Cancer of the sex organs is a sexually transmitted disease (F, p. 456).

28. Condoms provide some protection against VD (T, p. 453).

29. Fibroadenomas are one of the malignant breast tumors (F, p. 457).

30. The greater the number of sexual partners, the greater the chances of developing cervical cancer (T, p. 461).

31. Cervical cancer is rare among celibate women and lesbians (T, p. 461).

32. Every woman over the age of 20 should have an annual Pap smear for early detection of cervical cancer (T, p. 461).

33. Administration of testosterone helps to halt prostate cancer (F, p. 462).

34. Cancer of the penis is much more common among circumcized men than among uncircumcized men (F, p. 462).

CHAPTER 20: ETHICS, RELIGION, AND SEXUALITY

I. LEARNING OBJECTIVES

Study of this chapter should enable the student to:

1. Define the terms hedonism, asceticism, legalism, situationism, ataraxia, dualism, humanism.

2. Compare and contrast Old and New Testament views of sexuality.

3. Indicate how Joseph Fletcher's situation ethics and the "New morality" differs from the "Old morality."

4. Describe the different attitudes held toward sexuality by Jesus and each of the Christian thinkers who followed him.

5. Compare the Islam, Hindu, and Buddhist views of sex.

6. Describe the contemporary Christian position toward such issues as premarital and extramarital sex, contraception and abortion, and homosexuality.

7. Indicate Hyde's position regarding sexual ethics.

II. CHAPTER AT A GLANCE

Introduction (pp. 466-467): Sexual behavior is influenced by ethics and religion, and it is important to understand how they do so. Defines ethics, hedonism, asceticism, legalism, and situationism.

Sexuality in Great Ethical Conditions (pp. 467-478): Discusses the general view of sex in each of the following systems.
   Classical Greek Philosophy: Sex, though not necessarily evil, is something to be transcended.
   Judaism and the Old Testament
   The New Testament and Christianity
       Jesus
       St. Paul
       The early Christian Church
       St. Augustine
       St. Thomas Aquinas
       The Protestants
       Current trends
   Nontheistic Western Ethics
   Sexuality in Other Religions
       Islam
       Hinduism
       Buddhism

Contemporary Issues in Sexual Ethics (pp. 478-484)
       Premarital Intercourse
       Extramarital Sex
       Contraception
       Abortion
       Homosexuality

Toward an Ethics of Human Sexuality (pp. 484-486)

Summary (p. 486)

Suggestions for Further Reading (p. 487)

Focuses:

   Joseph Fletcher and Situation Ethics (p. 468)
   The Sin of Sodom (p. 483)

III. GLOSSARY

situation ethics. As defined by Joseph Fletcher, a way of making ethical decisions on the basis of the concrete situation and the people involved, rather than on the basis of rules.

IV. AUDIO-VISUAL AIDS

Movies:

Thank you mask man. Grove, 9 min., color, $200/$25. Animated
version of a Lenny Bruce routine which deals with sexual attitudes, obscenity and myth-making.

Tapes:

Sex and ethics. Norton, 60 min., $14.00. Dialogue between
attorney, rabbi, priest, and professor of comparative religion.
They discuss eccentric sexual practices, adultery, openness
and sex, conflicting cultural values, the concept of consent,
the meaning of humanism, and the distinction between law and
ethics.

V. DEMONSTRATIONS OR GROUP DISCUSSION

A. Guest speakers: Clergy. Invite 3 or 4 clergy to form a panel
and speak on their views on sexual ethics, as well as respond to
questions from the class. Ideally, the clergy should represent a
variety of religious traditions and a spectrum of liberalism-conser-
vatism, such as a rabbi, a Roman Catholic priest, a liberal Protestant, and a conservative Protestant.

B. Debating ethical issues. Have members of the class form debating teams on the issues covered in the second half of the chapter in
the text. After the teams work up their arguments, one or more de-
bates may be held before the whole class. Examples of resolutions
are:

1. There is nothing inherently unethical in premarital intercourse.
2. Extramarital sex is always immoral.
3. The use of contraception is an ethical obligation for responsi-
   ble sexuality.
4. Abortion is an absolute moral evil.
5. Homosexual behavior, in itself, is not immoral.

C. Values clarification - Premarital intercourse. Read the following scenario to students (or have copies available for everyone):
    Steve and Anne have been dating for several months. Although
they are very much in love, they have not yet had intercourse with
each other. They find themselves getting closer and closer to intercourse and want to know what is right. So they ask several people
for advice.
    Anne is a Roman Catholic, so she talks to her priest, Father
Flynn. He tells her that the Church teaches that sex outside of
marriage is always wrong. He advises her either to marry Steve or

let the relationship cool off. Chuck, Steve's fraternity brother, asks Steve what the big deal is. "If it feels good, do it" is Chuck's advice. Karen is Anne's older sister and advises her to be very careful. Karen thinks sex is only okay with someone you are probably going to marry. Her advice is to wait until Steve produces an engagement ring. Steve goes to see his minister, a liberal Protestant. Rev. Freeman tells him that the morality of premarital intercourse depends on the situation, the level of commitment between the couple, and their willingness to assume responsibility for their actions. He refuses to give them direct advice but urges them to talk the matter over carefully and make a decision they both feel is right. Roger and Jenny are grad students in psychology who live together. They tell Steve and Anne to think about the emotional consequences of sleeping together and whether or not they might wind up hurting each other. They say that a sexual relationship is great as long as no one is hurt.

Have students rank the five pieces of advice from 1 (best) to 5 (worst).

        Fr. Flynn   _____
        Chuck   _____
        Karen   _____
        Rev. Freeman   _____
        Roger and Jenny _____

Then have students discuss their rankings, either in small groups, or using the format described in the Introductory Values Clarification Exercise (Chapter 1 of this Manual).

VI. EVALUATION MATERIALS

Essay or research questions

1. Hyde proposes an ethics of human sexuality. Describe this position and indicate your reasons for agreement or disagreement with it. (See pp. 484-486.)

2. If you could choose one of the three non-Western religions as the one to which your parents and you belonged, which would you choose and why? (See pp. 476-478.)

3. Describe your own ethical position regarding any three of the following issues: premarital sex, extramarital sex, homosexuality, abortion or contraception. For one of these issues indicate the ways in which your position is similar to, and in disagreement with that taken by the Catholic Church. (See pp. 478-484.)

Multiple choice

1. ___: The belief that the ultimate goal of human life is the pursuit of pleasure, avoidance of pain and the fulfillment of physical needs and desires. a. asceticism; *b. hedonism; c. legalism; d. situationism. (p. 467)

2. ___: The belief that there is more to life than its material aspects, which must be transcended to achieve true humanity. *a. asceticism; b. hedonism; c. legalism; d. situationism. (p. 467)

3. ___: The belief in following some sort of law outside the individual such as nature or religion. a. asceticism; b. hedonism; *c. legalism; d. situationism. (p. 467)

4. ___: The belief that each ethical decision should be made according to the individual persons and situations involved. a. asceticism; b. hedonism; c. legalism; *d. situationism. (p. 467)

5. The Playboy Philosophy is probably closest to this stance. a. asceticism; *b. hedonism; c. legalism; d. situationism. (p. 467)

6. In the Old Testament, sexuality: a. is a deep and intimate part of a relationship between two people; b. can never be separated from its social consequences; c. is an aspect of national and religious loyalty; *d. all of the above. (pp. 469-470)

7. After an early life of promiscuity ___ converted to Christianity and began to preach a very negative view of sexuality, even in marriage. a. Jesus; *b. St. Augustine; c. St. Paul; d. St. Thomas Aquinas; e. none of the above. (p. 473)

8. ___ believed that procreation was the purpose of sex and that intercourse for any other purpose was sinful. a. Jesus; b. St. Augustine; c. St. Paul; *d. St. Thomas Aquinas; e. none of the above. (pp. 473-474)

9. ___ advocated celibacy as the demands of marriage might distract one from prayer. a. Jesus; b. St. Augustine; *c. St. Paul; d. St. Thomas Aquinas; e. none of the above. (p. 472)

10. In terms of its roots, the closest of the non-Western religions to the Judeo-Christian heritage is: a. Buddhism; b. Hinduism; *c. Islam; d. Taoism. (p. 476)

11. The highly positive view of sex in ___ is exemplified by the erotic Kama Sutra. a. Buddhism; *b. Hinduism; c. Islam; d. Taoism. (p. 477)

12. The prophet of this religion said very little about sexual conduct. *a. Buddhism; b. Hinduism; c. Islam; d. Taoism. (p. 478)

13. Celibacy is opposed in classical ___. a. Buddhism; b. Hinduism; *c. Islam; d. Taoism. (p. 476)

14. Extramarital intercourse is a sin, but polygymy and concubinage were sanctioned in ___. a. Buddhism; b. Hinduism; *c. Islam; d. Taoism. (p. 476)

15. Jesus allowed ___ to be grounds for divorce. a. infertility of one of the spouses; b. refusal to have intercourse by one of the spouses; *c. extramarital sex; d. all of the above; e. none of the above. (p. 479)

16. ___ is now acceptable in the Catholic Church. a. premarital sex by an engaged couple; b. artificial birth control; c. sterilization; d. divorce; *e. none of the above. (p. 479)

17. Any artificial means of contraception is now opposed by: a. Roman Catholics; b. Orthodox Jews; *c. both a & b; d. none of the above. (p. 480)

18. The Roman Catholic Church is adamant in its position that it is sinful to: a. be a homosexual; b. engage in homosexual acts; c. commit adultery; d. all of the above; *e. both b & c. (p. 482)

19. The "old morality" tends to be ___ in its approach to sexuality. a. ascetic; b. legalistic; c. hedonistic; *d. both a & b; e. both b & c. (p. 484)

20. The "new morality" tends to take a(n) ___ approach to sexuality. a. ascetic; b. hedonistic; c. situationist; d. both a & b; *e. both b & c. (p. 485)

True/False

1. The Old Testament view of sex is fundamentally positive (T, p. 469).

2. From examination of the teachings in the Book of Genesis, human sexual differentiation is really an afterthought (F, p. 469).

3. Situationism is the belief that the ultimate goal of human life is the pursuit of pleasure and avoidance of pain (F, p. 467).

4. Jesus said almost nothing on the subject of sexuality (T, p. 472).

5. The early Christian Church saw sexuality, even in marriage, as incompatible with true holiness (T, p. 473).

6. In his writings, St. Augustine sought to move the church toward a more permissive and accepting tolerance of sexual expression (F, p. 473).

7. The Protestant Reformation in the 16th Century maintained the requirement of clerical celibacy up until the end of the 18th Century (F, p. 474).

8. Humanistic ethics accepts no supernatural source, instead relying on human experience for moral direction (T, p. 475).

9. Homosexuality was viewed as particularly sinful in the Islamic religion (F, pp. 476-477).

10. The least ascetic of the non-Western religions described by Hyde is Buddhism (F, pp. 476-478).

11. Sterilization is now permissible in the Catholic Church (F, p. 479).

12. Orthodox Jews oppose artificial means of birth control (T, p. 480).

13. Up until the middle of the 1800's, abortion during the first 40 days after conception was permitted by the Catholic Church (T, p. 481).

14. According to the Roman Catholic Church, it is not necessarily sinful to be homosexual (T, p. 482).

15. The Roman Catholic hierarchy in England has endorsed decriminalization of homosexual acts between consenting adults (T, p. 482).

CHAPTER 21: SEX AND THE LAW

I. LEARNING OBJECTIVES

Study of this chapter should enable the student to:

1. Trace the reasons for sex laws from historical times to the present.

2. Describe the variety of acts that are covered under the different categories of sex laws.

3. Describe Packer's suggestions regarding laws of coercion.

4. Indicate how sex laws are enforced, and the reforms that Hyde suggests.

5. Describe the Wolfenden report including when and where it was written.

6. Specify the changes which have occurred as a result of each of the three major court decisions reviewed under the issue of right to privacy.

7. Indicate the principle involved in the reforms regarding "victimless crimes" and the crimes which fall under that category.

8. Give the definitions, popular and legal, of obscenity and pornography, and describe the various court decisions regarding obscenity.

9. Indicate how pornography affects behavior.

10. Describe Anthony Comstock's efforts regarding public and private morality.

11. Indicate what led to Oscar Wilde's trial and describe the reasoning behind the trial's outcome.

12. Describe Slovenko and Packer's contribution to our understanding of sex laws.

13. Define miscegenation.

14. Specify the issues and rulings in each of the following trials: Griswold v. Connecticut, Eisenstadt v. Baird, Roe v. Wade, Roth, Memoirs, Ginzburg, and Miller v. California.

II. CHAPTER AT A GLANCE

Introduction (p. 490)

Why Are There Sex Laws? (pp. 490-491): Describes both "legitimate" and more questionable reasons, including the protection of public morals.

What Kinds of Sex Laws Are There? (pp. 491-499): Notes that a complete catolog would be very difficult.
Crimes of Exploitation and Force: Includes rape and sex with children.
Criminal Consensual Acts: These laws were designed to protect marriage and the family and include laws against fornication, cohabitation, adultery, miscegenation, sodomy.
Crimes Against Taste: Includes laws against exhibitionism, voyeurism, solicitation, disorderly conduct, prostitutes, homosexuals and "sexual psychopaths."
Crimes Against Procreation: Includes laws pertaining to contraception and abortion.
Criminal Commercial Sex: Includes laws against prostitution and obscenity.

Sex-Law Enforcement (p. 499): Notes that this is with great inconsistency and arbitrariness.

Trends in Sex-Law Reform (pp. 499-507): Change in this area is occurring very rapidly.
Early Efforts at Sex-Law Reform: Describes the English Wolfenden report and the American Law Institute's Moral Penal Code recommendations.
Right to Privacy: Describes Griswold v. Connecticut (contraceptive advice to married couples by physicians), Eisenstadt v. Baird (contraceptive advice to unmarried persons), Roe v. Wade (abortion), Doe v. Commonwealth Attorney (homosexual acts).
Victimless Crimes: Uses prostitution as example.
The Problem of Obscenity and Pornography: Gives definitions, describes U.S. v. Roth, Miller v. California, and the findings of the Commission on Obscenity and Pornography.

Summary (pp. 507-508)

Suggestions for Further Reading (p. 508)

Focuses:

Anthony Comstock: Crusader Against Vice (pp. 492-493)
The Trial of Oscar Wilde (pp. 500-501)

III. GLOSSARY

fornication. Sexual intercourse between two unmarried people.

obscenity. Something that is offensive according to accepted standards of decency; the legal term for pornography.

pornography. Sexually arousing art, literature, or films.

sodomy. An ambiguous legal term which may refer to anal intercourse, sexual relations with animals, or mouth-genital sex.

IV. AUDIO-VISUAL AIDS

Movies:

Sex for sale: The urban battleground. CRM McGraw-Hill, 45 min., color, $695/$70. A look at several major urban centers where x-rated sex--in the form of magazines, films, prostitution, and massage parlors--has become big business and has created both big civil, legal, and moral rights questions. This film should be shown after students are familiar with the chapter as the instructor can ask students to evaluate critically the assumptions and conclusions of the film.

Freedom to love. Grove, 90 min., color, $1250/$90. Phyllis and Eberhard Kronhausen's film about the irrationality of common sexual prejudices and traditional sex laws. Argues that sexual freedom does not pose a danger to society.

Dirty business. Multi Media, 25 min., color. Interviews with the actors, audience, attorneys and producers of hardcore pornography.

Tapes:

Sex and the law. Norton, #340279, 60 min., $14.00. A series of interviews with different people on their attitudes regarding four issues including age and consentuality, prostitution, sex discrimination, and pornography and censorship. The tape ends with a discussion of criminal law and family law.

Pornography and fantasy. Norton, #340171, 60 min., $14.00. Presents the three-part obscenity ruling by the Supreme Court and discusses the difficulties of trying to interpret it. Gives examples of different cultural concepts of what might or might not be art or pornography. Describes the research on the effect on behavior of exposure to pornography.

V. DEMONSTRATIONS OR GROUP DISCUSSION

A. Speaker on legal issues. Ask someone from the local branch of the ACLU to discuss legal action in your area on privacy law, victimless crimes, and sexual preference discrimination.

B. Values clarification/consensus exercise. Divide the class into groups of 6-8. The task of each group is to come to a consensus on what sexual behavior the law should regulate. Include in the discussion the following, plus any other areas you find appropriate.
Prostitution
Sodomy
Homosexual acts
Abortion
Rape
Obscenity and Pornography
Note that the exercise requires students to reach a consensus. This process ought to dramatize the difficulty of framing legislation in an area in which the values of Americans are so much in disagreement.

VI. EVALUATION MATERIALS

Essay or Research questions

1. Describe any four sexual acts which are currently against the law and indicate your opinion as to whether or not each of them should be illegal. (See pp. 492-499.)

2. Summarize the arguments for and against the obscenity laws and give your opinion as to the extent you believe these laws should be maintained. (See pp. 497-499, 505-507; students may want to consult Psychological Abstracts for a research paper on the latest findings regarding the influence of exposure to erotica on subsequent behavior.)

3. Describe the changes in the legal status of abortion in the 1970's and indicate the conditions under which you believe abortion should be legal. (See p. 503.)

Multiple choice

1. Kinsey estimated that ___ of males in his sample had engaged in illegal acts. a. 15%; b. 35%; c. 65%; *d. 95%. (p. 490)

2. Packer has argued that all but one of the following should be rationally included in law. Which would he not include?
*a. laws against prostitution and other behaviors which conflict with accepted standards of morality; b. laws against force or coercion for sex; c. protection of the immature against sexual

exploitation; d. prevention of conduct that gives offense or is likely to give offense to innocent bystanders. (pp. 490-491)

3. Currently, ___ appears to have the most laws regulating sexuality. a. England; b. France; c. Sweden; *d. the United States. (p. 491)

4. At present, there are ___ laws regulating American sexual behavior. a. 1,050; b. 2,500; c. 5,000; d. 25,000; *e. none of the above; we really don't know how many there are. (p. 491)

5. Rape and sex relations with the young are: *a. crimes of exploitation and force; b. criminal consensual acts; c. crimes against taste; d. crimes against procreation. (p. 492)

6. Anthony Comstock was: a. an English pornographer; b. a homosexual who appealed his conviction to the Supreme Court; c. a physician convicted of giving contraceptive information; *d. a special agent of the U.S. Post Office who lobbied for passage of a comprehensive antiobscenity law. (p. 492)

7. According to the standard legal definition of rape: a. either gender can be a rape victim; b. a husband can be tried for raping his wife; c. ejaculation is necessary; *d. a man can be tried for raping a woman from whom he is legally separated. (p. 493)

8. Comstock did not work for: *a. laws against the employment of homosexuals; b. a congressional bill which prohibited the mailing of obscene material; c. a congressional bill prohibiting ads for obscenity; d. laws to prohibit verbally giving contraceptive information. (pp. 492-493)

9. Statuatory rape laws prohibit: a. a male from having intercourse with a female under the age of 17; b. a male from having intercourse with a female under the age of 12; c. a male from having intercourse with a female under the age of consent providing that she was previously a virgin; *d. a male over 17 or 18 from having intercourse with a female under the age of consent regardless of her previous sexual history or consent. (p. 494)

10. Child molestation laws may include: a. physical or genital contact; b. use of sexual language; c. exhibitionism; d. showing a child pornography; *e. all of the above. (p. 494)

11. In the United States, incest is illegal in: a. about half of the states; b. about three-quarters of the states; c. all but two states; *d. every state. (p. 494)

12. When Playboy summarized state laws in 1972, ___ was illegal and punishable by jail sentences of up to 5 years in a majority of the states. a. cohabitation; b. adultery; c. fornication; d. miscegenation; *e. both a & b. (p. 495)

13. When Playboy summarized state laws in 1972, adultery was grounds for divorce in ___ states. a. 23; b. 26; c. 41; *d. all. (p. 495)

14. Laws against miscegenation (sex between members of different races) regardless of their marital status: a. presently exist in nine states in the south; b. existed in about half the states until the Supreme Court invalidated them in 1977; *c. existed in about half the states until the Supreme Court invalidated them in 1967; d. have not existed since the Civil War; e. have never existed in the United States. (p. 495)

15. Statutes against sodomy can include: a. oral-genital sex; b. anal-genital sex; c. bestiality; d. both b & c; *e. all of the above. (p. 496)

16. Consensual sodomy is illegal: a. in France; b. in most of Europe; c. in the Soviet Union; d. in the United States; *e. both c & d. (p. 497)

17. Exhibitionism, voyeurism, solicitation, and "general lewdness" are illegal under: a. crimes of exploitation and force; b. criminal consensual acts; *c. crimes against taste; d. crimes against procreation; e. criminal commercial sex. (p. 497)

18. Prostitution is illegal in: a. every state in the U.S.; b. almost all countries; *c. every state but Nevada; d. both a & b; e. both b & c. (p. 497)

19. Obscenity laws attempt to: a. prevent corruption of morals by materials that incite sexual thoughts and desires; b. ensure that no one will profit by the production and distribution of such materials; c. discourage consumption of such materials by punishing the consumer; *d. both a & b; e. all of the above. (p. 499)

20. Since private consensual sex offenders are rarely arrested, Hyde argues that movements for reform of the sex laws: a. aren't particularly necessary; b. are important since the threat of prosecution penalizes the "offender;" c. are important since uneven enforcement of sex laws may have a very bad effect on law enforcement generally; *d. both b & c. (p. 499)

21. The Wolfenden committee recommended decriminalization of: *a. homosexuality; b. dispensing contraceptive information and devices; c. abortion; d. distribution of pornography. (p. 501)

22. The Supreme Court invalidated a state law in which a physician
    was prosecuted for providing contraceptive information, instruc-
    tion and advice to a married couple in: a. Eisenstadt v. Baird;
    *b. Griswold v. Connecticut; c. Roe v. Wade; d. Miller v. Cali-
    fornia. (p. 502)

23. The court invalidated a Massachusetts state law forbidding dis-
    semination of contraceptive information to the unmarried in:
    *a. Eisenstadt v. Baird; b. Griswold v. Connecticut; c. Miller
    v. California; d. Roe v. Wade. (p. 502)

24. The court agreed that the right of personal privacy includes the
    abortion decision, and made the right to first trimester abor-
    tion nearly absolute, in: a. Eisenstadt v. Baird; b. Griswold
    v. Connecticut; c. Miller v. California; *d. Roe v. Wade.
    (p. 503)

25. According to Hyde, police enforcement of prostitution laws:
    a. is expensive; b. is unsuccessful; c. is open to corruption;
    d. both a & c; *e. all of the above. (pp. 504-505)

26. Oscar Wilde was convicted for: *a. homosexual behavior; b. per-
    forming illegal abortions; c. writing pornographic books;
    d. producing pornographic movies. (p. 500)

27. Hyde notes that obscenity is: *a. a legal term and pornography
    is a popular term; b. a popular term and pornography is a legal
    term; c. protected by the First Ammendment according to the
    Supreme Court; d. both a & c. (p. 505)

28. The Supreme Court defined obscenity as material which deals with
    sex in a manner appealing to prurient interest in the ___ case.
    a. Memoirs; b. Miller v. California; *c. Roth; d. Zarathustra.
    (p. 506)

29. The Supreme Court ruled that community standards could determine
    what is obscene in: a. Griswold v. Connecticut; *b. Miller v.
    California; c. Roth; d. Morton v. Kansas. (p. 507)

30. Pornography: a. has temporary adverse effects on people; b. con-
    sumers tend to be more deviant than non-consumers; *c. does not
    seem to lead to pathological behavior in the long run; d. all of
    the above. (p. 507)

31. The 1970 report of the Commission on Obscenity and Pornography
    recommended prohibitions on the distribution of sexually expli-
    cit material to: a. children; b. unconsenting adults; c. consent
    ing adults; *d. both a & b; e. all of the above. (p. 507)

1. Ralph Slovenko is a legal scholar concerned with laws regarding sexuality (T, p. 490).

2. The existence of laws regulating sexual conduct have been taken for granted during most of Western history (T, p. 490).

3. Historically, laws against fornication were designed to assure children of a supportive family by reducing out-of-wedlock births (T, p. 491).

4. Much of American law regarding sexuality was derived from the French legal system (F, p. 491).

5. The English believed that as protectors of the interests of the church, morality was a matter of public and legal responsibility (T, p. 491).

6. Since 1800, there has been a trend toward increased legal regulation of sexual behavior in many societies, and in contrast with our society (F, p. 491).

7. According to the standard legal definition of rape, either gender may be a rape victim (F, p. 493).

8. In a rape trial, the consent of the victim is the principal issue (T, p. 493).

9. A man has not committed rape when he forces a woman with whom he is legally separated to have intercourse according to the standard legal definition of rape (F, p. 493).

10. A rape victim's prior sexual activities are considered as evidence of her consent in many states (T, p. 493).

11. Laws against incest assign penalties in proportion to the closeness of the relationship (T, p. 494).

12. All anti-miscegenation laws were invalidated by the Supreme Court (T, p. 495).

13. The highest sentence for sodomy in any of the states is ten years (F, p. 496).

14. The Comstock laws included a ban on giving contraceptive information (T, p. 497).

15. Prostitution is illegal in every jurisdiction in the U.S. (F, (p. 497).

16. The Wolfenden Report recommended that heavier penalties be exacted for prostitution from both the prostitute and her customer (F, p. 501).

17. In Doe v. Commonwealth Attorney, the Supreme Court affirmed a lower court decision that Virginia could constitutionally prohibit homosexual acts (T, p. 503).

18. Victimless crimes account for over half the cases handled by American courts (T, p. 504).

19. Approximately one-third of the VD in the U.S. is attributable to prostitution (F, p. 505).

20. In Ginzburg, the Supreme Court overturned a lower court conviction of a publisher for flagrantly exploiting the sexually arousing nature of his publication in ads (F, p. 506).

21. Following the complete decriminalization of sexually explicit material in Denmark, there was a marked reduction in child molestation and a number of other sexual crimes (T, p. 507).

CHAPTER 22: SEX EDUCATION

I. LEARNING OBJECTIVES

Study of this chapter should enable the student to:

1. Indicate preferred and actual sources of sex education for young people.

2. Describe the kind of research that has been conducted on the effects of formal sex education and indicate what these studies have found.

3. Know the nine SIECUS goals in teaching young people about sexuality.

4. Specify the qualities Hyde believes are important for a sex education teacher.

5. Describe Piaget's three stages of understanding about reproduction.

6. Know the level of sex knowledge of children across different cultures.

7. Describe Bernstein's findings regarding the six levels of knowledge about reproduction.

8. Indicate what children's "dirty" jokes suggest about their attitudes toward sexuality and toward interaction with their parents on sex education.

9. Describe the principles that are important for any sex education curriculum and give examples of how the sample curriculum in the text demonstrates these principles.

II. CHAPTER AT A GLANCE

<u>Introduction</u> (p. 510)

<u>In the Home, In the School, or Somewhere Else</u> (pp. 510-511): Notes that most information comes from peers, though most young people would prefer to get their sex education from their parents.

<u>Effects of Sex Education</u> (pp. 511-512): Reviews the research.

<u>Purposes of Sex Education</u> (p. 512): Presents goals listed by SIECUS.

<u>The Teacher</u> (pp. 512-514): Hyde describes qualifications she thinks are important.

<u>What to Teach at Different Ages</u> (pp. 514-522): Suggests the process should begin when children are small.
<u>A Theoretical View: Piaget</u>: Describes three stages of understanding of reproduction.
<u>Children's Sex Knowledge</u>: Cross-cultural research is presented.
<u>Signs of understanding</u>: Describes Bernstein's research and 6-stage theory.
<u>Children's questions about sex</u>
<u>Children's dirty jokes</u>

<u>Curriculum</u> (pp. 522-523): Covers three principles that are important for sex education curricula.

<u>Summary</u> (p. 523)

<u>Suggestions for Further Reading</u> (p. 523)

<u>Focuses</u>:

<u>Questions Children Ask About Sex</u> (pp. 516-518)
<u>A Sample Sex Education Curriculum</u> (pp. 520-521)

III. GLOSSARY

None of the terms used in this chapter should be unfamiliar to students.

IV. AUDIO-VISUAL AIDS

Movies:

<u>Dangling Participle</u>. Grove, 17 min., B & W, $150/$20. Parts of old sex education films are blended in a humorous, satiric fashion. Demonstrates some of the sources of our current sexual attitudes.

<u>Sex and the Professional</u>. Texture, 25 min., color, $385/$45.
   This film was produced for the professional who intends to
   teach students and patients about sex, and is aimed at helping professionals accept their own sexual feelings and impulses.

<u>A Three Letter Word for Love</u>. Texture, 27 min., color, $330/$35.
   Presents inner-city teenagers talking about their sexual
   knowledge, fantasies, experience and misconceptions.

<u>Tapes</u>:

<u>Sex Education</u>. Norton, #340236, 60 min., $14.00. Parents express
   their concerns regarding sex education including who will
   teach, what will be taught, and why and how sex education
   should be taught. Samples of elementary school sex education
   are presented and formal and informal sex education is discussed.

V. DEMONSTRATIONS OR GROUP DISCUSSION

   <u>Role play</u>: Telling your daughter/son about sex. The purpose of
this exercise is to give students some beginning practice at communicating about sex with their offspring, and to stimulate them to
begin thinking about how they might best do it when the actual situation arises.
   Mrs. Black is 30 and college-educated. She has decided that it
is time to sit down with her daughter, Susie, a fifth grader, to tell
her about sex.
   Have students role play this situation (see General Instructions
for Role Plays, Chapter 14 of this Manual). Following the role
play, students may want to proceed to a more general discussion of
sex education in the home, how it could be done better than in the
situation above, what they think the ideal course of action would
be, and so on.

VI. EVALUATION MATERIALS

Essay or research questions

1. Describe and evaluate your own sex education in terms of the proportion of accurate information you received from the various sources noted in your text. Describe the approach to sex education you
would take with your own child and indicate how it differs from your
sex education. (See pp. 510-511.)

2. Describe the kinds of studies that have been conducted on the
effects of formal sex education. What are the general results of
these studies and what can we infer about the effects of sex

education given the kinds of studies that have been conducted?
(See pp. 511-512.)

3. Describe one of the first sexual ("dirty") jokes you heard as you were growing up and analyze it for the presence or absence of the three themes that tend to be reflected in children's dirty jokes. (See p. 522.)

Multiple choice

1. The primary source of sex information for most children is:
   a. parents; b. reading; *c. friends; d. school program;
   e. adults outside the home. (p. 510)

2. The source of sex education that young people would prefer is:
   *a. parents; b. reading; c. friends; d. school program;
   e. adults outside the home. (p. 510)

3. Sex education in the schools is related to: a. a decrease in premarital pregnancy; b. a dramatic decrease in promiscuity; c. a reduction in the incidence of gonorrhea; d. general psychological adjustment; *e. both c & d. (p. 512)

4. SIECUS is an organization devoted to: a. promoting gay rights; b. professionalizing prostitution; c. legalizing abortion; *d. promoting sex education; e. none of the above. (p. 512)

5. In Piaget's theory about the development of children's understanding of reproduction, ___ is the last stage. *a. naturalistic; b. scientific; c. adult; d. preartificialistic; e. artificialistic. (p. 512)

6. A very small proportion (2% or less) of Israeli children aged $4-5\frac{1}{2}$: *a. mentioned intercourse as a source of babies; b. could describe the sex organs of the opposite gender; c. knew that babies came from the mother's enlarged belly; d. both a & b; e. all of the above. (p. 514)

7. When asked what a mother does to get a baby, many $4-5\frac{1}{2}$ year old Israeli children mentioned: a. eating a lot; b. swallowing a baby; c. have intercourse; d. contacting the stork; *e. both a & b. (p. 514)

8. In the study of Israeli children's sex knowledge, children of non-Western ancestry: a. knew a great deal more than the children of European and American ancestry; *b. knew a great deal less than the children of European and American ancestry; c. did not differ in the amount of knowledge from the children of European and American ancestry; d. none of the above. (pp. 514-515)

9. Bernstein found that children progress through a series of levels of understanding about reproduction. At level three, transitional, they believe that: a. a baby has always existed; b. the father must make love to the mother for the baby to come out of him and into her; c. a manufacturing process is involved; *d. the father contributes something which feeds and helps protect the baby (like a shell). (pp. 515, 518-519)

10. "Well, the father puts the shell. I forget what its called, but he puts something in for the egg. If he didn't, then a baby couldn't come. Because it needs the stuff that the father gives...." This is an example of level ___ from Bernstein's research on children's understanding of reproduction. a. 1, geography; b. 2, manufacturing; *c. 3, transitional; d. 4, concrete physiology; e. 5, preformation. (pp. 515, 518-519)

11. A typical question children ask in 10th, 11th and 12th grades is: a. Why can't I marry Daddy? *b. What is a virgin? c. Do you menstruate the rest of your life once you start? d. Do boys menstruate? e. How does the sperm get into the egg? (p. 518)

12. In the Sample Sex Education Curriculum, the use of correct terminology such as "penis" and "breast" is taught: *a. in kindergarten and grade 1; b. in grades 2 and 3; c. in grades 4 or 5; d. in grades 6 or 7; e. in grades 8 or 9. (p. 520)

13. Children's dirty jokes tend to reflect all but one of the following themes. According to Zumwalt which is not reflected? a. belief that parents are trying to keep sex a secret from them; b. fascination with sex; *c. belief that sexual intercourse is painful; d. satirization of adults' use of euphemisms for sexual terms. (p. 522)

14. According to Hyde, a sex education curriculum should cover: a. the biological aspects of sex; b. the emotional aspects of sex; c. the social aspects of sex; *d. all of the above; e. both a & c. (p. 523)

15. According to Hyde, sex education should begin: *a. in kindergarten or 1st grade; b. in 3rd or 4th grade; c. in 5th or 6th grade; d. in 7th or 8th grade; e. in 9th or 10th grade. (pp. 522-523)

True/False

1. The majority of parents oppose sex education in the schools (F, p. 511).

2. Females who have had sex education in school tend to be less sexually experienced than females who have not (T, p. 512).

3. Institution of sex education programs in schools reduced the incidence of gonorrhea by as much as 50% in a year's time (T, p. 512).

4. One of the sex education goals of SIECUS is to work for a society in which such evils as prostitution and illegitimacy, archaic sex laws, irrational fears of sex, and sexual exploitation are nonexistent (T, p. 512).

5. Hyde believes that it is crucial that sex educators have doctoral level training since the field is so broad (F, p. 513).

6. According to Piaget, during the earliest phases of understanding about reproduction (ages 3-5) children believe that a baby has always existed (T, p. 514).

7. According to Piaget, during the earliest phases of understanding about reproduction (ages 3-5) children believe that parents cause the creation of babies, although they may have some bizarre ways of explaining how parents do this (F, p. 514).

8. A recent study found that the majority of American children aged 3-5½ years knew that the father had a role in reproduction (F, p. 515).

9. Bernstein found that not until they are 12 or older do children reach level 6, physical causality, in which they give a good explanation of reproduction (T, p. 519).

10. Hyde argues that sex education should be given at every grade level beginning in fourth grade (F, p. 522).

11. According to Hyde, correct terminology for the sex organs should be taught from the beginning in kindergarten and first grade (T, p. 522).

CHAPTER 23: SEXUALITY IN THE FUTURE

I. LEARNING OBJECTIVES

Study of this chapter should enable the student to:

1. Describe the major future changes which are likely to affect our sexuality.

2. Indicate the extent to which we have successfully developed such techniques as artificial insemination, sperm banks, embryo transplants, test-tube babies, cloning, and gender-selection.

3. Describe Hyde's predictions regarding lifestyle changes in sexuality (hetero-, homo-, and bi-).

4. Specify what is meant by "hot sex" and "cool sex".

5. Indicate possible ways in which role behaviors for the genders will shift and specify which areas are likely to change more slowly.

6. Describe the hard decisions that Hyde believes we face.

II. CHAPTER AT A GLANCE

<u>Introduction</u> (p. 526): The two main areas in which changes are ocurring are in technologies and lifestyles.

<u>Technologies</u> (pp. 526-528)
  <u>Artificial Insemination</u>: About 1% of American children today were conceived this way.
  <u>Sperm Banks</u>: Currently used by men prior to vasectomies or cancer treatment.
  <u>Embryo Transplants</u>: Successful since 1975 with primates, but not yet possible with humans.
  <u>Test-Tube Babies</u>: Although Hyde predicted a breakthrough "within a few years," she completed writing the text just prior to July, 1978 when the first "test-tube" baby was born in England.
  <u>Cloning</u>: Notes that it isn't yet scientifically feasible.
  <u>Choosing Your Baby's Gender</u>: Mentions Shettles work as one of the current sources of investigation in this area.

<u>Lifestyles</u> (pp. 528-530): Could predict the emergence of one of two trends: continuation of the liberalization of sex or a reactionary backlash toward sexual conservatism.
  <u>Heterosexuality</u>
  <u>Homosexuality and Bisexuality</u>
  <u>Hot Sex and Cool Sex</u>: Analogizes from McLuhan.
  <u>Gender Roles</u>: Movement toward androgyny?
  <u>Some Hard Decisions</u>: Suggests that it would be best to decide what we want our future sexuality to be like and then shape our technology and lifestyles to fit that decision rather than passively allowing the reverse process.

III. GLOSSARY

<u>artificial insemination</u>. The injection, by means of an instrument, of semen into a woman's vagina or uterus for the purpose of inducing pregnancy.

<u>cloning</u>. Producing many genetically identical individuals from a single parent.

IV. AUDIO-VISUAL AIDS

<u>Movies</u>:

<u>The family: Lifestyles of the future</u>. Document, 21 min., color, $300/$40. Presents review of alternatives to the conventional family including visits to the rural Perth Conspiracy, a 50-member family who live communally; a small urban family where

two couples share all the responsibilities involved in work and child-rearing; and a "three-way family" consisting of a man and two women. Dr. Margaret Mead offers insights into the nature of the rebellion against the nuclear family, explaining why divergent forms of family life are needed, and why the family of the future will have to be a "great shock absorber."

Tapes:

New life styles. Norton, #340260, 60 min., $14.00. Suggests that various new life styles have far-reaching implications for the family, society, and the individual. Presents examples and discusses their sexual advantages and disadvantages including college coed living, a daughter seeking permission to spend a weekend away with her boyfriend, multiple marriage among four individuals, and a child of a commune asking why he can't be like others with only one set of parents.

V. DEMONSTRATIONS OR GROUP DISCUSSION

Dialogue: Hard decisions. In the final chapter, it is suggested that we can passively allow technology and shifts in lifestyles to alter our sexuality, or we can decide what we want our sexuality to be like in the future and then shape our technology to our values. Hyde suggests a quote from the Francoeurs as a beginning to the latter strategy: "The question is, which modification will be most humane, most functional, most growth-promoting...."
Present this quote to students and ask them to divide into groups of 6-8. Give each group one of the technological issues and ask them to decide what policies they would recommend regarding their issue, if any.
Specific questions could include:
1. Should taxes be used to support research in this area?
2. What limits would you impose on scientists working in this area?
3. Who should control the information and techniques which are developed?
4. What are the major moral and social issues which might arise should this technique be developed?
After each group has discussed their issue, ask them to present their decisions to the class and ask for a vote regarding each decision. This should demonstrate some of the difficulties in trying to develop rational strategies in dealing with such possibilities as cloning, test-tube babies, embryo transplants, etc.

VI. EVALUATION MATERIALS

Essay or research questions

1. Select one of the areas in which scientists are presently working for breakthroughs, indicate the state of our knowledge with that technique, and give your opinion as to what limits, if any, should be placed on the development and use of that particular technique. (See pp. 526-528.)

2. Hyde describes four ways in which lifestyles appear to be changing. Choose one of these areas, describe Hyde's prediction and indicate whether you think the predicted change is an improvement or not, and why you feel that way. (See pp. 528-530.)

Multiple choice

1. Hyde suggests that development of the birth control pill has: a. contributed to the liberation of women; b. influenced changes in gender roles; c. influenced changes in sexual behavior and attitudes; d. both a & c; *e. all of the above. (p. 526)

2. According to your text, ___ is not yet possible with humans. a. freezing sperm; b. artificial insemination; c. embryo transplants; d. cloning; *e. both c & d. (pp. 526-527)

3. Sperm were frozen without any apparent damage to them: a. in the late 1800's; b. in the early 1900's; *c. in the mid 1900's; d. none of the above; sperm have not yet been successfully frozen. (p. 526)

4. Artificial insemination was first successfully done with animals about the time of: *a. the American revolution (1776); b. the Civil War (1860); c. the first World War (1917); d. the second World War (1941); e. none of the above. (p. 526)

5. Embryo transplants have been unsuccessful with: a. cattle and rabbits; b. baboons; *c. humans; d. both b & c; e. all of the above. (p. 527)

6. Hyde predicts: a. a reactionary backlash toward sexual conservatism; b. an increase in homosexuality; *c. an increase in extramarital sex; d. a decrease in divorce; e. both a & d. (p. 528)

True/False

1. Although artificial insemination by a donor other than the husband is theoretically possible, it has not yet been done, as it is illegal (F, p. 526).

2. About 1% of all children born in the U.S. today are conceived by means of artificial insemination (T, p. 526).

3. Although it is possible to freeze and store sperm, there are only two sperm banks available in the U.S. (F, p. 527).

4. Sperm banks are being used by young men to store sperm before they undergo radiation treatment for cancer (T, p. 527).

5. In cloning, no sperm is necessary (T, p. 528).

6. Cool sex is highly property-oriented whereas hot sex is highly person-oriented (F, p. 529).

CHAPTER 24: FINAL COMPREHENSIVE EXAM MATERIAL

I. LEARNING OBJECTIVES

This final set of learning objectives is designed to help the student synthesize what has been learned during the course. Toward this goal, several strategies are suggested for retaining much of the information beyond the final exam.

1. Although it may be difficult to remember the precise percentages of individuals who engage in various sexual behaviors or who hold particular sexual attitudes, students should know which behaviors and attitudes tend to be normative, and which tend to be typical of a minority of the population. Thus, the student might want to list the various sexual behaviors and attitudes covered in the text and indicate which are characteristic of the majority versus the minority of the population.

2. The student should be familiar with the major studies of each of the various aspects of sexuality including (a) who conducted them; (b) the primary conclusions from these studies; (c) the kind of evidence on which the conclusions are based; and (d) the theoretical perspective (when possible) which guided each of the studies. Students may test their knowledge of these points by reviewing the names of contributors from each of the previous lists of learning objectives.

3. The Glossary, beginning on p. 531 of the text, may be used for review of those terms which were unfamiliar to the student at the beginning of the course.

4. The student should be able to describe the name, location, and function of each of the parts of the male and female sexual anatomy.

5. In addition to knowing the distinction between stereotypic and "real" gender differences, the stucent should be able to specify the similarities and differences between the genders which were described throughout the text.

6. Finally, students should be able to specify those cultural beliefs which are, and are not, supported by scientific evidence, as well as those areas which have not yet been scientifically investigated.

II. EVALUATION MATERIALS

Essay Questions

The following statements are culturally held beliefs. In response to each, indicate when possible: (a) the kind of evidence available regarding the statement; (b) who gathered the evidence; and (c) how the evidence does or does not support the statement.

1. You can usually tell that someone is homosexual by the way they behave.

2. Career women are lacking in femininity and aren't very interested in sex.

3. "Porno" stores and movies should be closed down because they lead to rape.

4. Women who can't "come" without direct manual or oral stimulation of the clitoris are fixated at any early stage of development.

5. The idea that men really choose women on the basis of physical attractiveness is just a notion cooked up by the advertising industry to sell products.

6. Women who take the birth control pill for a couple of years have a hard time getting pregnant when they go off the pill.

7. You can catch gonorrhea from toilet seats, but you don't have to worry too much about it since the disease has been pretty much eliminated by antibiotics.

8. Humans are the only species to engage in forms of sexual activity that may not result in reproduction (for instance, homosexuality, oral sex, etc.).

9. "Opposites attract" and both men and women are more interested in a person who plays hard to get.

10. People usually stop having intercourse after they reach their sixties, and this is particularly true of people who have "over-indulged" by having sex a lot when they were young.

11. Women shouldn't be permitted to engage in any sort of demanding or dangerous work during the week prior to their menstrual period.

12. Masturbation leads to impotency.

13. If you give children much information about sex, they will be more likely to be promiscuous than if you wait until just before they get married.

Contributors and their contributions

1. Which of these people relied on actual observation of behavior?
   a. Kinsey; *b. Masters & Johnson; c. Hunt; d. Sorensen;
   e. Kantner & Zelnick.

2. Which of these people conducted research in the lab? a. John Alan
   Lee; b. Sorensen; *c. Heiman; d. Humphreys; e. Hite.

3. Which of these people conducted research in the field? a. Heiman;
   b. Masters & Johnson; c. John Money; *d. Humphreys; e. both a & c.

4. Which doesn't belong with the others? a. Masters & Johnson;
   b. Kaplan; *c. Berscheid & Walster; d. LoPiccolo & Lobitz.

5. Which of these used the best sampling techniques? *a. Hunt;
   b. Hite; c. Kinsey; d. Maslow; e. Fletcher.

6. Which of these conducted research based on a psychoanalytic perspective? a. Bieber; b. Wolff; c. Humphreys; d. Kinsey;
   *e. both a & b.

7. Which of these most violated the principle of informed consent?
   a. Kinsey; b. Hunt; *c. Humphreys; d. Lamaze; e. Hite.

8. Which of these doesn't belong with the others? a. Maslow; b. John
   Alan Lee; *c. Hunt; d. Fromm; e. C. E. Lewis.

9. Which of these employed experimental manipulation? a. Martin &
   Lyon; *b. Schmidt & Sigusch; c. Pietropinto & Simenauer; d. Hite;
   e. Freud.

10. Which of these provided cross-cultural observations? a. Zick Rubin;
    b. Cohen; *c. Ford & Beach; d. Cuber; e. both a & b.

11. Which of these used a large sample? a. Hunt; b. Kinsey; c. Kantner
    & Zelnick; d. Sorensen; *e. all of the above.

12. Which of these doesn't belong with the others? *a. Joseph Fletcher;
    b. Kinsey; c. Hunt; d. Sorensen; e. Kantner & Zelnick.

13. Which of these was concerned with gender roles? a. Zick Rubin;
    b. Kallman; c. Bem; d. Broverman; *e. both c & d.

14. Which of these based their conclusions on a sample of adults?
    a. Kantner & Zelnick; b. Piaget; c. Bernstein; *d. Westoff; e. all
    of the above.

15. Which of these studied the phenomenon of rape? a. Burgess & Holm-
    strom; b. Cohen; c. Kallman; d. all of the above; *e. both a & b.

16. Which doesn't belong with the others? a. Bieber; b. Wolff;
    c. Kallman; *d. Heiman; e. Humphreys.

17. Which of these conducted follow-up studies to examine the influ-
    ence of participation in research on subjects' well-being?
    a. Hooker; *b. Masters & Johnson; c. Horner; d. Bart; e. all of
    the above.

18. Which of these was concerned with gender reassignment? a. Kinsey;
    b. Broverman; *c. John Money; d. Reiss; e. Paige.

19. Which of these tested the genetic explanation of homosexuality
    via examination of twins? *a. Kallman; b. Dick-Read; c. Erikson;
    d. Bell; e. Cuber.

20. Which of these found that females reported substantially less
    arousal than males to erotic materials? a. Heiman; b. Schmidt &
    Sigusch; c. Westoff; *d. Kinsey; e. all of the above.

21. Which of these explored the relationship between menopause and
    depression? *a. Bart; b. Kantner & Zelnick; c. Weinberg & Williams;
    d. Broverman; e. Pietropinto & Simenauer.

22. Which of these used only females in their sample? a. Kantner &
    Zelnick; b. Hite; c. Wolff; d. Burgess & Holmstrom; *e. all of
    the above.

23. Which of these used only males in their sample? a. Pietropinto &
    Simenauer; b. Weinberg & Williams; c. Sorensen; d. all of the
    above; *e. both a & b.

24. Which of these proposed a 6-level description of children's
    understanding of reproduction? a. Piaget; *b. Bernstein; c. Kap-
    lan; d. Bieber; e. both a & b.

25. Which of these emphasized theory and/or ideas rather than
    research? a. Freud; b. Joseph Fletcher; c. C. E. Lewis; d. Erik-
    son; *e. all of the above.

26. Which of these was concerned with marital styles? a. Lamaze;
    *b. Cuber; c. Sorensen; d. Hooker; e. none of the above.

27. Which of these has been cited as using excellent interviewing
    techniques? *a. Kinsey; b. Kallman; c. Maslow; d. Schmidt &
    Sigusch; e. none of the above.

28. Which of these may contain serious sampling problems? a. Hite;
    b. Weinberg & Williams; c. John Alan Lee; d. all of the above;
    *e. both a & b.

29. Which of these excluded homosexuals from the sample? a. Kinsey; b. Hunt; c. Weinberg & Williams; d. Wolff; *e. none of the above.

30. Which of these used the concepts "femininity-achievement-incompatibility" and "fear of success?" a. Wolff; b. Kaplan; c. Pietropinto & Simenauer; *d. Horner; e. Broverman.

31. Which of these developed a pencil/paper measure of androgyny? a. Horner; *b. Bem; c. Martin & Lyon; d. Humphreys; e. none of the above.

32. Which of these developed a pencil/paper measure of love? a. Bell; *b. Zick Rubin; c. Bem; d. Maslow; e. none of the above.

33. Which of these measured physiological arousal rather than relying only on self-report? a. Hunt; b. Heiman; c. Masters & Johnson; d. Kaplan; *e. both b & c.

34. Which of these studied menstrual cycle mood fluctuations? a. Bem; *b. Paige; c. Broverman; d. Horner; e. both a & b.

35. Which of these hypothesized that love is a function of physiological arousal and appropriate cognitive labeling? a. Piaget; b. Fromm; *c. Berscheid & Walster; d. Zick Rubin; e. both c & d.

36. Which of these was concerned primarily with animal sexuality? a. Masters & Johnson; b. Horner; c. Kaplan; d. Bieber; *e. none of the above.

37. Which studied adolescent contraceptive behavior? *a. Kantner & Zelnick; b. Hooker; c. Zick Rubin; d. LoPiccolo & Lobitz; e. none of the above.

38. Which of these originated the clitoral/vaginal orgasm distinction? a. Fromm; b. Masters & Johnson; c. Maslow; d. Kinsey; *e. none of the above.

39. Which of these made a distinction between Being-love and Deficiency-love? *a. Maslow; b. Bart; c. Freud; d. Fromm; e. John Alan Lee.

40. Which of these used the concept of spectatoring? a. Bernstein; *b. Masters & Johnson; c. Cohen; d. Burgess & Holmstrom; e. Bem.

41. Which of these uses masturbation training for the treatment of orgasmic dysfunction? a. Schmidt & Sigusch; b. Weinberg & Williams; c. Pietropinto & Simenauer; *d. LoPiccolo & Lobitz; e. Burgess & Holmstrom.

42. Which of these observed behavior as it occurred rather than experimentally manipulating variables? *a. Humphreys; b. Heiman; c. Schmidt & Sigusch; d. all of the above; e. both b & c.

Gender Differences and Similarities

Indicate if each of the following is more typical of males, more typical of females, or if no reliable gender differences have been found, by using the code below.

A = Males are more likely than females.....

B = Females are more likely than males.....

C = There are no reliable differences due to gender in the tendency.....

1. To inflict pain on their partner during sexual arousal and intercourse (p. 18, B).

2. To experience monthly cyclicity in hormone levels (p. 51, B).

3. To engage in homosexual behavior across different cultures (p. 19, A).

4. To experience acne during adolescence (p. 67, A).

5. To use a variety of masturbation techniques (p. 186, B).

6. To have fantasies while they masturbate (p. 187, A).

7. To become sexually aroused when exposed to erotic material, according to the Kinsey studies (p. 227, A).

8. To become sexually aroused when exposed to erotic material, according to contemporary studies (p. 227, C).

9. To report an increase in their coital activity following exposure to erotica, according to Schmidt, Sigusch, & Schafer's study (p. 227, B).

10. To obtain information about masturbation from peers during preadolescence (p. 238, A).

11. To obtain information about masturbation from self-discovery during preadolescence (p. 238, B).

12. To increase the frequency with which they masturbate when they are (compared to when they aren't) involved in heterosexual activity (p. 241, B).

13. To decrease the frequency with which they masturbate when they are (compared to when they aren't) involved in heterosexual activity (p. 241, A).

14. To attach significance to their first sexual experience (p. 246, A).

15. To engage in premarital sex (p. 243, A).

16. To report feelings of maturity and joy after first sexual intercourse, according to Sorensen (p. 246, A).

17. To participate in homosexual relations while engaged in "swinging" (p. 265, B).

18. To be the reason why elderly couples stop having intercourse according to the wives (pp. 268-269, A).

19. To be the reason why elderly couples top having intercourse according to the husbands (pp. 268-269, A).

20. To report a great deal of satisfaction with marital sex (p. 259, A).

21. To be aggressive during early childhood (p. 282, A).

22. To excel in spatial ability during early childhood (p. 282, C).

23. To have adjustment problems in elementary school (p. 285, A).

24. To adjust well to elementary school (p. 285, B).

25. To be high in self-esteem as adults (p. 287, A).

26. To excel in mathematical ability (p. 287, A).

27. To excel on tests of verbal abilities (p. 287, B).

28. To excel on tests of spatial ability (p. 287, A).

29. To excel on tests of general intelligence (p. 287, C).

30. To disclose information about themselves (pp. 288-289, B).

31. To interrupt the person with whom they are having a conversation (pp 288-289, A).

32. To be pressured to conform to gender role expectations during childhood (p. 282, A).

33. To have considerable freedom regarding conformity to gender role expectations during childhood (p. 282, B).

34. To have psychotherapy (p. 284, B).

35. To lack confidence in their abilities (p. 287, B).

36. To stand close to same-sexed persons (p. 289, B).

37. To have orgasm each time they have intercourse (pp. 296-297, A).

38. To report masturbating in Kinsey's study (p. 298, A).

39. To report masturbating in Hunt's study (p. 298, A).

40. To rate erotic tapes as arousing according to Heiman (p. 300, B).

41. To be unaware of their own sexual arousal in Heiman's study (p. 300, B).

42. To reach the "peak" of their sexual desire in late adolescence (pp. 299-300, A).

43. To reach the "peak" of their sexual desire in their thirties (pp. 299-300, B).

44. To have masturbation as their first sexual experience (p. 307, A).

45. To have heterosexual petting as their first sexual experience (p. 307, B).

46. To believe in a double standard regarding the acceptability of premarital sex in Hunt's sample (p. 304, B).

47. To engage in homosexual behavior with a large number of different partners in their lifetime (p. 329, A).

48. To have a homosexual experience (pp. 332-333, A).

49. To be transvestites (p. 359, A).

50. To request gender reassignment via surgery (pp. 352-353, A).

51. To get high love scores (that is, to report feeling love for their partner) in Rubin's study (p. 400, C).

52. To have their popularity determined by their physical attractiveness (p. 404, B).

53. To have their desirability determined by their success (pp. 404-405, A).

54. To like the people they love, according to Rubin (p. 400, B).

55. To have early stage gonorrhea with no symptoms (p. 444, B).

56. To get cystitus (p. 456, B).

Sexual Norms

Indicate whether or not each of the following is normative by placing an A or B in front of each phrase.

A = A majority of.....

B = A minority of.....

1. Societies regulate sexual behavior (pp. 15-18, A).

2. Societies condemn incest (pp. 15-18, A).

3. Societies condemn forced sexual relations (pp. 15-18, A).

4. Societies approve of adult masturbation (pp. 18-19, B).

5. People engage in homosexual behavior in every society (p. 19, B).

6. Cultures find thinness (compared to plumpness) attractive (p. 20, B).

7. Conceptions are female (p. 47, B).

8. Conceptions are male (p. 47, A).

9. Women experience a menstrual cycle which lasts 28 days (p. 73, B).

10. Women experience mood fluctuations during the menstrual cycle (pp. 77-78, A).

11. Women experience severe menopausal symptoms (p. 83, B).

12. Species are characterized by female estrous (rather than menstrual) cycles (p. 70, A).

13. The cases of spasmodic dysmenorrhea occur during the ages of 26-40 (p. 75, B).

14. The cases of spasmodic dysmenorrhea occur during the ages of 15-25 (p. 75, A).

15. Women who have mood fluctuations are in a positive mood around the time of ovulation (p. 76, A).

16. The acts of violence and suicide committed by women occur in the eight premenstrual and menstrual days of the cycle (p. 77, A).

17. The acts of violence and suicide committed by women occur in the week during which they ovulate (p. 77, B).

18. The babies born at the beginning of the 7th month after conception will survive (p. 97, B).

19. The babies born in the middle of the 8th month after conception will survive (p. 97, A).

20. Pounds gained during pregnancy (not counting the baby) come from increased retention of fat and water (p. 103, A).

21. Pounds gained during pregnancy (not counting the baby) come from enlargement of the uterus (p. 103, B).

22. American mothers breast-feed their infants (p. 117, B).

23. Spontaneous abortions occur because the fetus is defective (p. 121, A).

24. Spontaneous abortions occur because of psychological trauma to the woman (p. 121, B).

25. Spontaneous abortions occur because of physical traumas to the mother (p. 121, B).

26. Women using birth control pills use the sequential pill (p. 129, B).

27. Women using the birth control pill experience an increase in sexual desire (pp. 133-134, B).

28. Women using the birth control pill experience a decrease in sexual desire (pp. 133-134, B).

29. Women experience guilt and shame after abortion (p. 153, B).

30. Deaths due to abortion occur with the suction method (p. 153, B).

31. Catholics use artificial methods of contraception (p. 129, A).

32. Women become pregnant within one year if they have intercourse without any contraception (p. 135, A).

33. Cancers of the reproductive organs are a result of contraceptive use (pp. 129-138, B).

34. The conceptions occurring to diaphragm users are due to improper use rather than failure of the method (p. 139, A).

35. American men have masturbated (p. 186, A).

36. American women have masturbated (p. 186, A).

37. Our information about sexual behavior has come from experimental research (p. 207, B).

38. Our information about sexual behavior has come from people's self-reports of their sexual practices (p. 207, A).

39. Kinsey's sample were Catholics (p. 213, B).

40. Males engage in homosexual play during preadolescence (p. 239, A).

41. Females engage in homosexual play during preadolescence (p. 239, B).

42. Adolescents who have any homosexual experience have their first homosexual act with a person their own age (pp. 242, 320, A).

43. Adolescents who have any homosexual experience have their first homosexual act with an adult (pp. 242, 320, B).

44. Adolescents engaging in premarital sex say they do so for the physical pleasure (pp. 247-248, B).

45. Women in Hunt's sample who engaged in premarital sex did so with only one partner (pp. 248-249, A).

46. Women in Hunt's sample who engaged in premarital sex did so with two or more partners (pp. 248-249, B).

47. The adolescents who have homosexual experiences prefer homosexuality as adults (p. 241, B).

48. The preadolescents who have homosexual experiences prefer homosexuality as adults (p. 241, B).

49. Males in Hunt's sample engaged in premarital sex (pp. 243, 304-305, A).

50. Males in Kinsey's sample engaged in premarital sex (pp. 304-305, A).

51. Females in Kinsey's sample engaged in premarital sex (pp. 304-305, B).

52. People in Hunt's sample approved of premarital sex (pp. 304-305, A).

53. Females in Hunt's sample engaged in premarital sex (pp. 243, 304-305, A).

54. People in Hunt's sample engaged in premarital sex (pp. 243, 304-305, A).

55. Married women who engaged in premarital sex regret having done so (p. 249, B).

56. Noncohabitants in the Cornell study gave "ethical reasons" as their motives for not cohabiting (p. 251, B).

57. Cohabitants in the Cornell study described their relationship as a "trial marriage" (p. 251, B).

58. Americans marry (p. 256, A).

59. Married women wish that they had intercourse more often (p. 260, B).

60. Married women wish that they had intercourse less frequently (p. 260, B).

61. Married men wish that they had intercourse more often (p. 260, B).

62. Married men wish that they had intercourse less frequently (p. 260, B).

63. Women engage in extramarital sex (p. 263, B).

64. Those couples who "swing" find their partners by "converting" non-swinging couples (p. 265, B).

65. Married couples in Hunt's sample engaged in oral sex (p. 258, A).

66. Swingers are politically liberal (p. 265, B).

67. Swingers are politically conservative (p. 265, A).

68. Divorced women who engage in postmarital sex do so within a year of the divorce (p. 267, A).

69. Widowed women who engage in postmarital sex do so within a year of their husband's death (p. 267, A).

70. Women aged 20-55 hold paying jobs (p. 283, A).

71. Males describe "love" for the girl as their reason for engaging in intercourse for the first time (p. 298, B).

72. Sexually active girls in the 1970s consistently use contraceptives (p. 305, B).

73. Males in Pietropinto & Simenauer's study indicated that they were irritated by a woman who seemed cold or uninterested while having sex (p. 311, A).

74. Males in Pietropinto & Simenauer's study indicated that they were irritated by a woman who made the first advance (p. 311, B).

75. Males in Pietropinto & Simenauer's study indicated that they were irritated by a woman who made demands (p. 311, B).

76. Males in Pietropinto & Simenauer's study indicated that they were irritated by a woman who seemed "too easy" (p. 311, B).

77. Hite's subjects had orgasm without separate massaging of the clitoris (p. 309, B).

78. Americans believe that homosexuality is harmful to American life (p. 317, A).

79. Americans believe that homosexuality is a curable illness (p. 317, A).

80. Homosexual males may be recognized by their effeminate behavior (p. 319, B).

81. Homosexual males are masculine sex-typed (p. 319, A).

82. Homosexual females may be recognized by their "masculine" behavio (p. 319, B).

83. Homosexual couples in on-going relationships play roles that mirror heterosexual gender roles (p. 319, B).

84. Child molesting is done by heterosexual males (p. 320, A).

85. Child molesting is done by homosexual males (p. 320, B).

86. The homosexuals in Humphrey's Tearoom Trade study used interfemor intercourse (p. 331, B).

87. The homosexuals in Humphrey's Tearoom Trade study used anal inter course (p. 331, B).

88. Studies seeking the cause of homosexual behavior and/or genetic factors have not found such a relationship (pp. 337-339, A).

89. Males who are raised by a dominant mother become homosexual (p. 343, B).

90. Americans approve of legalizing private, homosexual behavior between consenting adults (p. 317, B).

91. Homosexuals believe that homosexuality is an illness (p. 318, B).

92. Gay bars are gender-integrated (serve both male and female homo-sexuals) (p. 326, B).

93. Homosexuals can be identified by skilled clinicians on the basis of their responses to a projective personality measure (p. 336, B).

94. Transvestites are heterosexual (p. 359, A).

95. Transvestites are homosexual (p. 359, B).

96. Exhibitionists attempt rape (p. 362, B).

97. Child en have been approached by child molesters (p. 363, B).

98. Child molesters use force on the children (p. 363, B).

99. Child molesters are friends of, or related to, the child (p. 363, A).

100. Cases of incest are between fathers and their daughters (p. 364, B).

101. Cases of incest are between brothers and sisters (p. 364, A).

102. Call girls are from lower class backgrounds (p. 370, B).

103. Call girls are heterosexual in their private lives (p. 370, A).

104. Prostitutes are street walkers (p. 370, A).

105. Prostitutes are call girls (p. 370, B).

106. Transsexuals are generally very happy in their new gender (p. 355-356, A).

107. Child molesters are from the middle class (p. 364, B).

108. Prostitutes were forced into the profession (p. 371, B).

109. Rapes are reported to police (p. 376, B).

110. Rapists are under 25 (p. 382, A).

111. Rapists murder their victims (pp. 382-383, B).

112. Rapists are of the sex-aggression-fusion type (pp. 383-384, B).

113. The studies of interpersonal attraction have examined relation-ships which have been going on for a year or more (p. 408, B).

114. The studies of interpersonal attraction have focussed on relationships during their formative stages or on initial responses to strangers (p. 408, A).

115. The studies of interpersonal attraction support the notion that "similarity attracts" (p. 403-404, A).

116. The studies of interpersonal attraction support the notion that "opposites attract" (p. 403-404, B).

117. Masters and Johnson's male clients sought treatment for premature ejaculation (p. 413, B).

118. Women seeking help from Masters and Johnson complained of orgasmic dysfunction (p. 416, A).

119. The sexual dysfunctions are caused by organic and/or biological factors (p. 417, B).

120. The sexual dysfunctions are caused by learned (psychological) factors (p. 417, A).

121. Masters and Johnson's clients are successfully treated (p. 431, A).

122. The cases of erectile dysfunction are due to physiological causes (p. 417, B).

123. Diabetic men have erectile dysfunction (p. 419, B).

124. Reported cases of gonorrhea are for the 15-29 year old age group (p. 443, A).

125. Women have no symptoms during the early stages of gonorrhea (p. 444, A).

126. Men with trichomoniasis are asymptomatic (p. 455, A).

127. Breast lumps are benign (p. 457, A).

128. Breast lumps are cancerous (p. 457, B).

129. Female cancers occur in the cervix (p. 461, B).

130. The Christian rules regarding sexual behavior came from Jesus' teachings (p. 472, B).

131. The males in Kinsey's sample had engaged in illegal sex acts (p. 490, A).

132. States have laws against cohabitation (p. 495, A).

133. States have laws against adultery (p. 495, A).

134. States allow adultery as grounds for divorce (p. 495, A).

135. Private consensual offenders are arrested for their illegal sex acts (p. 499, B).

136. The cases handled by American courts involve "victimless crimes (p. 504, A).

137. The cases of VD are contracted through prostitutes (p. 505, B).

138. Children get their information about sex from school teachers (p. 510, B).

139. Children get their information about sex from friends (p. 510, A).

140. Children get their information about sex from their parents (p. 510, B).

141. Children would prefer to get their information about sex from parents (p. 510, A).

142. Children would prefer to get their information about sex from friends (p. 510, B).

143. Children would prefer to get their information about sex from school teachers (p. 510, B).

144. Parents oppose sex education in the schools (p. 511, B).

145. Parents approve of sex education in the schools (p. 511, A).

Multiple Choice

1. Which of these has the least to do with love? *a. phimosis;
   b. philia; c. storge; d. eros; e. agape.

2. The dark area of skin surrounding the nipple of the breast is
   called the: a. agape; *b. areola; c. edema; d. follicle; e. corona.

3. The findings from research on the severity of women's menopausal
   symptoms is most inconsistent with the beliefs of: a. Mangaians;
   *b. people of Inis Beag; c. Europeans; d. Americans; e. Kerakians.

4. ___ is an early symptom of syphilis. a. chancroid; b. condom;
   *c. chancre; d. areola; e. pheromones.

5. Research indicates that fluctuations in women's ___ occur with
   the phases of the menstrual cycle. a. productivity at work;
   b. athletic performance; *c. mood; d. all of the above; e. none
   of the above.

6. ___ is a sexual variation in which arousal is associated with
   defecation or feces. a. gametes; b. urophilia; c. satyriasis;
   *d. coprophilia; e. dysmenorrhea.

7. The major discipline which has contributed to our understanding
   of human sexuality is: a. anthropology; b. biology; c. psychology;
   d. sociology; *e. all of the above.

8. This watery substance is secreted from the breasts at the end of
   pregnancy and during the first few days after delivery. a. estrous
   *b. colostrum; c. conceptus; d. amniotic fluid; e. corpus luteum.

9. It is 1988, and the Democrats, Republicans, and Independents have
   all chosen relatively young female candidates as their candidates
   for President. If you subscribe to the notion that women's
   "raging hormonal shifts" render them unfit for the job, your best
   bet is to vote for the woman who is___ and using ___ birth control
   pills. *a. Protestant, combination; b. Catholic, sequential;
   c. Jewish, sequential; d. agnostic, combination; e. Catholic, no.

10. Which of these doesn't belong with the others? a. lymphogranuloma
    venereum; b. monilia; *c. lochia; d. trichomoniasis; e. vaginitis.

11. Bartell's conclusions about swinging were based on: a. experimental manipulation of variables; *b. participant observation;
    c. a large scale survey; d. physiological measures of responses;
    e. both c & d.

12. Foreskin is also known as: a. follicle; *b. prepuce; c. priapism;
    d. prenatal; e. circumcision.

13. ___ is a rare condition in which erections are longlasting and painful. a. urophilia; b. troilism; *c. priapism; d. spirochete; e. granuloma inguinale.

14. Hunt's conclusions regarding sexual behavior were based on: a. experimental manipulation of variables; b. theoretical speculation; *c. a large scale survey; d. cross cultural research; e. physiological measures of responses.

15. ___ refers to before birth. *a. prenatal; b. prepuce; c. pediculosis pubis; d. multiparous; e. priapism.

16. The area between the vaginal opening and the anus is called the: a. pheromone; *b. perineum; c. placenta; d. phimosis; e. priapism.

17. Paige's study of mood fluctuations in menstrual cycles involved: a. experimental manipulation of variables; b. cross cultural research; c. participant observation; d. all of the above; *e. none of the above.

18. ___ is a hormone secreted by the pituitary which is involved in lactation. a. luteinizing hormone (LH); b. testosterone; c. human chorionic gonadotropin (HCG); *d. prolactin; e. interstitial cell stimulating hormone (ICSH).

19. We may conclude that premarital masturbation causes women to have orgasm earlier in marriage from: a. Kinsey's study of sexual behavior; b. Hunt's study of sexual behavior; c. LoPiccolo & Lobitz's masturbation therapy study; d. both a & b; *e. none of the above.

20. This gland is located below the bladder and secretes most of the fluid in semen. a. prolactin; b. Cowper's gland; c. epididymis; d. seminiferous tubules; *e. prostate.

21. We may conclude that premarital masturbation is related to the length of time it takes women to have orgasm after marrying from: *a. Kinsey's study of sexual behavior; b. Cuber's study of types of marriage; c. Fromm's study of love; d. Zick Rubin's study of love; e. Heiman's study of arousal.

22. Chemical substances that are secreted outside the body and are important in communication between animals are called: a. spirochetes; *b. pheromones; c. vaginismus; d. phimosis; e. perineums.

23. Reiss' study of standards regarding premarital sex over the past few decades suggests that: a. the norm of chastity until marriage never really existed; b. the norm of chastity until marriage remains among the upper classes; *c. we now endorse a norm of permissiveness with affection; d. in the under 25-year-old age group, "anything goes;" e. none of the above.

24. ___ is a condition in which the foreskin is so tight that it cannot be retracted. a. onanism; b. priapism; *c. phimosis; d. urophilia; e. myotonia.

25. The length of time following childbirth is the: a. menarche; b. multiparous period; c. nulliparous period; *d. postpartum period; e. menstrual period.

26. A person who feels that he or she is trapped in the body of the wrong gender is called a(n): a. transvestite; b. homosexual; *c. transsexual; d. androgyn; e. all of the above.

27. ___ is an organ formed on the wall of the uterus through which the fetus receives oxygen and nutrients. a. seminiferous tubules; b. zygote; c. ovary; d. lochia; *e. placenta.

28. Kelly, Tracy, and Kim meet every Saturday night to have intercourse together. Their behavior is known as: a. transsexuality; b. monilia; c. tumescence; *d. troilism; e. satyriasis.

29. Bem's research on androgyny involved: a. experimental manipulation of variables; b. cross-cultural research; c. injections of testosterone; d. injections of estrogen;*e. administration of a pencil/paper personality measure.

30. Swelling due to congestion with body fluids is called: a. prepuce; b. myotonia; *c. tumescence; d. phimosis; e. vaginismus.

31. John has been aware of arousal around young boys for some time, but he doesn't seek help until after he has seduced a 13-year old boy. The therapist calls the behavior _____ and gives him a serie of electric shocks while showing him pictures of boys in a process known as ___ therapy. *a. pederasty, aversion; b. pediculosis pubis, aversion; c. priapism, transactional analysis; d. satyriasis, psychoanalytic; e. onanism, punishment.

32. Childbirth is called: a. lactation; b. gestation; c. myotonia; *d. parturition; e. pedophilia.

33. Kantner & Zelnick's conclusions regarding contraceptive use are limited to: a. adolescent males; b. married women; *c. adolescent females; d. married males; e. contraceptive choices after clients have received abortions.

34. ___means sexual variation: a. monilia; b. lactation; *c. paraphilia d. zygote; e. phimosis.

35. This research is flawed by the fact that most of the subjects were obtained from particular kinds of organizations. a. Hite's study of female sexuality; b. Weinberg & Williams' study of homosexuals; c. Hunt's study of sexual behavior; d. all of the above; *e. both a & b.

36. To procure a prostitute for a client; sometimes used to mean any catering to another's sexual desires. a. voyeurism; b. priapism; c. pedophilia; d. phimosis; *e. pander.

37. Lolita's lover might be characterized as having this sexual variation. a. pheromones; b. pediculosis pubis; *c. pedophilia; d. prepuce; e. monilia.

38. This cheesy substance forms under the foreskin of the penis. *a. smegma; b. spirochete; c. pediculosis pubis; d. nulliparous; e. epididymis.

39. Schmidt, Sigusch, & Schafer's research on arousal to erotic material involved: *a. experimental manipulation of variables; b. participant observation; c. theoretical speculation; d. a large scale survey; e. none of the above.

40. ___ is a hormone secreted by the testes which maintains secondary sex characteristics. a. oxytocin; b. human chorionic gonadotropin (HCG); *c. testosterone; d. prolactin; e. interstitial cell stimulating hormone.

41. John and Mary have been fondling one another for some time, and when she gets up to get her diaphragm out of her dresser, she notices a rashlike condition on her skin which is called: a. smegma; b. priapism; c. monilia; d. urophilia; *e. sex flush.

42. The ___ are two organs lying on either side of the prostate. *a. seminal vesicles; b. epididymis; c. seminiferous tubules; d. pheromones; e. phimosis.

43. What problem does the research by Psychology Today, Redbook, and Shere Hite have in common? a. inferior interviewing techniques; b. failure to provide informed consent; c. exclusion of male responses; *d. sampling error due to volunteer bias; e. all of the above.

44. ___ refers to an extraordinarily high level of sex drive in a male. a. troilism; *b. satyriasis; c. nymphomania; d. onanism; e. prepuce.

45. Freud's contribution to sexuality involved bringing discussion of sex out of the closet, and: a. experimental manipulation of variables; b. participant observation research; c. conducting of large scale surveys; *d. theoretical speculation; e. all of the above.

46. ___ is a condition in which orgasm in the male is not accompanied by external ejaculation; instead, the ejaculate goes into the bladder. *a. retrograde ejaculation; b. retarded ejaculation; c. priapism; d. vasocongestion; e. troilism.

47. On the basis of Heiman's research on arousal to erotic material, we may conclude that: a. such arousal is limited to modern, industrialized societies; b. women are embarrassed to admit it when they feel aroused; *c. that women are sometimes unaware of their own arousal; d. that males are more affected by erotica than females are; e. all of the above.

48. The ___ are highly coiled tubules in the testes that manufacture sperm. a. seminal vesicles; b. Cowper's glands; *c. seminiferous tubulus; d. pediculosis pubis; e. inguinal canals.

49. Burgess & Holmstrom's conclusions regarding rape victims' responses are based on: *a. clinical observations; b. experimental manipulation of variables; c. participant observation; d. physiological measures of responses; e. none of the above.

50. Secretion of milk from the female's breasts is called: a. oxytocin; b. myotonia; *c. lactation; d. parturition; e. gestation.

51. ___ are cells in the testes which manufacture male sex hormones. a. interstitial cells; b. Leydig cells; c. seminal vesicles; d. Cowper's glands; *e. both a & b.

52. The research least likely to be based on a learning theory explanation of behavior was conducted by: a. John Money; b. Masters & Johnson; c. Bem; *d. Kallman; e. both a & b.

53. This is a discharge from the uterus and vagina that occurs during the first few weeks after childbirth. *a. lochia; b. smegma; c. zygote; d. gametes; e. estrous.

54. Testosterone has been used effectively: a. before the female-to-male sex change operation; b. after the female-to-male sex change operation; c. with homosexual males who want to become heterosexual; d. all of the above; *e. both a & b.

55. ___ is the passageway from the abdomen to the scrotum through which the testes usually descend shortly before birth. a. seminal vesicles; b. seminiferous tubules; c. vas deferens; *d. inguinal canal; e. interstitial cells.

56. The work on love by Maslow and by Fromm has in common: a. the experimental manipulation of variables; *b. theoretical speculation; c. conclusions based on questionnaire responses; d. physiological measures of response; e. none of the above.

57. ___ is a hormone secreted by the pituitary which causes ovulation: a. human chorionic gonadotropin (HCG); *b. luteinizing hormone (LH); c. interstitial cell stimulating hormone (ICSH); d. oxytocin; e. prolactin.

CHAPTER 25: AUDIO-VISUAL SOURCES

The names and addresses of the distributors of films described in this manual are presented below. In addition, you may want to write to the Unitarian Universalist Association for a description of their kit "About Your Sexuality" ($135.00 with materials for a class of 20 students). The kit contains (as abridged from UUA's description) a set of 12 leader's guides covering suggested units on: How to Begin the Program, Birth Control, Femininity and Masculinity, Love Making, Making Out, Male and Female Anatomy, Homosexual Life Styles, Masturbation, Same-Sex Relationships, Conception and Childbirth, and Venereal Disease, as well as a special guide outlining the methodology of the program and suggested adult programs. Also included are one copy of Fundamentals of Human Sexuality by Herant A. Katchadourian & Donald T. Lunde, Boys and Sex and Girls and Sex by Wardell B. Pomeroy, Society and the Healthy Homosexual by Dr. George Weinberg, and Lesbian/Woman by Del Martin & Phyllis Lyon.

Cinema Medica, Inc., 664 N. Michigan, Suite 600, Chicago, IL, 60611, (313) 664-6170.

CRM McGraw-Hill Films, 110 15th St., DelMar, CA, 92014, (714) 453-5000.

Center for Marital & Sexual Studies (CMSS), 5199 E. Pacific Coast Hwy., Long Beach, CA, (213) 597-4425.

Document Associates, Inc., 800 Third Ave., New York, NY 10022, (212) 593-1647.

Focus International, Inc., 505 West End Ave., New York, NY, 10024.

Grove Press Films, 196 West Houston St., New York, NY, 10014, (212) 242-4900.

Media Guild, Box 881, Solana Beach, CA, 92075.

Multi-Media Resource Center, 1525 Franklin St., San Francisco, CA, 94109.

Pennsylvania State University Audio-Visual Services, 6 Willard Bldg., University Park, PA, 16802.

Polymorph Films, 331 Newberry St., Boston, MA, 02115, (617) 262-5960.

Texture Films, 1600 Broadway, New York, NY, 10019, (212) 586-6960.

Unitarian Universalist Association, 25 Beacon St., Boston, MA, 02108.

The Williams & Wilkins Co., Audio-Visual Sales Dept., 428 East Preston St., Baltimore, MD, 21202.